b – last fa

.5⁰

The American Singer

♩ walking.
♩ slow
♪ running

dor # & b –
further to R – called ti –

The American Singer

✩ ✩ BOOK FOUR ✩ ✩

John W. Beattie

DEAN, THE SCHOOL OF MUSIC, NORTHWESTERN UNIVERSITY

EVANSTON, ILLINOIS

Josephine Wolverton

ASSISTANT SUPERVISOR, EVANSTON SCHOOLS

ASSISTANT PROFESSOR, THE SCHOOL OF MUSIC, NORTHWESTERN UNIVERSITY

EVANSTON, ILLINOIS

Grace V. Wilson

DIRECTOR OF MUSIC, PUBLIC SCHOOLS, WICHITA, KANSAS

Howard Hinga

ASSISTANT DIRECTOR OF MUSIC, PUBLIC SCHOOLS

INSTRUCTOR OF PUBLIC SCHOOL MUSIC, EASTMAN SCHOOL OF MUSIC

ROCHESTER, NEW YORK

✩ ✩ ✩

American Book Company

NEW YORK   CINCINNATI   CHICAGO

BOSTON   ATLANTA   DALLAS   SAN FRANCISCO

Beattie and others, The American Singer, Book Four

E. P. 12

Made in U. S. A.

To the Boys and Girls

As you sing these songs, you will be learning good music and also something about the people who have helped to build our America.

Acknowledgments

Grateful acknowledgment is made to publishers, authors, and individuals for permission to reprint the following material used in this book:

"OLD PAINT," "THE OLD GRAY MARE," and "LONE STAR TRAIL" from *American Ballads and Tunes* by John A. Lomax, The Macmillan Company.

"ROLLING KING" and "BLOW, YE WINDS" from *Roll and Go* by Joanna C. Colcord, Bobbs–Merrill Company.

"THE GREEN BUS" and "TRUCKS" from *I Go a-Traveling* by James Tippett, Harper and Brothers.

"SEA SHELL" by Amy Lowell, copyright, Houghton Mifflin Company.

Professor Henry Crew for the poem "NOBODY KNOWS" by Helen Coale Crew.

"BROOMS" from *Everything and Anything* by Dorothy Aldis, G. P. Putnam's Sons.

We are also indebted to the following for special services and suggestions:

Mr. and Mrs. Charles Seeger for assistance in the field of American folk songs and games.

Rosa Marti for French and Swiss songs and games.

Dorothea Jorgensen for Danish songs.

Dr. H. O. Hofmeyr for translation of the South African song, "Siembamba."

Chi Tung Tsu for Chinese songs.

René Amengual for contributing and translating Chilean songs and games.

Jakobina Johnson for contributing and translating Icelandic songs.

Timothy Fetler for contributing and translating Latvian and Russian songs.

Ruth Taylor and her class at Foster School, Evanston, Illinois, for their "Song of Thanks."

Elsie Ward and her class at Dewey School, Olive Clark and her class at Lincolnwood School, Evanston, Illinois, for their co-operation in trying out the material for final selection in this book.

Elizabeth Waterman for her continuing help with our rhythm program.

ILLUSTRATIONS BY CORINNE MALVERN AND JANET SMALLEY.

The American Singer
BOOK FOUR

Music in the New World

After the early voyages of Columbus and other explorers, the Americas were colonized, settled, and developed by people from the Old World. Some came in search of gold or land; some came in search of religious or political freedom; and many more came to make homes in new and uncrowded countries. From whatever region these immigrant forefathers of ours came and wherever they settled, they brought along their legends, songs, dances, and games. These they handed down through their children and their children's children. So America became a great storehouse of Old World folklore.

In this book you will find many songs and dances which originally were created in distant lands, as well as many which were composed here by our early settlers. You will find sailor chanteys and cowboy ballads. And you will enjoy songs of our South American neighbors and music written by modern composers.

The American Way

J. W. Beattie   ROTE   J. W. Beattie

With spirit

Tramp, tramp, tramp, hear the feet of man - y chil - dren

From the moun - tain, riv - er, and shore!

Who with smil - ing fac - es take their school - room plac - es

With their friends and neigh - bors once more.

Tramp, tramp, tramp, hear the feet of man - y chil - dren,

Thir - ty mil - lion read - y to - day!

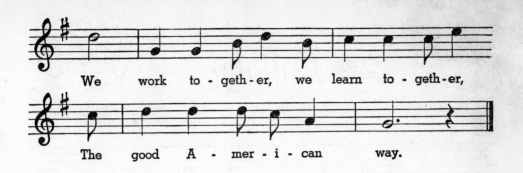

We work to-geth-er, we learn to-geth-er,

The good A-mer-i-can way.

Sing and Dance

Julie Gibault   ROTE   Czech Folk Dance

Happily

Come sing a song with a rol-lick-ing mel-o-dy,

Whirl in a dance while the mu-sic plays on;

Skies are blue, sun shines thro', na-ture's in har-mo-ny;

Come sing a song with a rol-lick-ing tune!

Lullaby

ROTE

Translated

Brahms

Gently

1. Lull - a - by and good night,
2. Lull - a - by and good night,

In the soft eve - ning light,———
Let the an - gels of light———

Like a rose in its——— bed,
Bring in dream - land for——— thee

Lay——— down——— your sweet head;
The——— Christ——— Child's own tree;

When the morn - ing is here,
Now sleep well, close your eyes,

I will wake you, my dear,
Dream of sweet Par - a - dise,

When the morn - ing is here,
Now sleep well, close your eyes,

I will wake you, my dear.
Dream of sweet Par - a - dise.

 # White Butterflies

Swinburne   ROTE   Rossetter G. Cole

With quick, graceful motion

1. Fly, white but - ter - flies,— out to sea,
2. Some fly light— as a laugh of glee,

Frail, pale wings— for the wind to try;
Some fly soft— as a low, low sigh;

Small white— wings that we scarce can see,
All to the ha - ven where each would be,

1.
Fly, fly, fly!

2.
Fly, fly, fly!

A Frog Went a-Courtin'

Traditional　　　　　　**ROTE**　　　　　**Tennessee Version**

Brightly

1. A frog went a-court-in', he did ride, h' m, h' m,
2. He rode till he came to Mouse-'s hall, h' m, h' m,

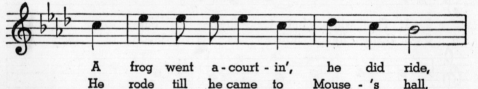

A frog went a-court-in', he did ride,
He rode till he came to Mouse-'s hall,

Sword and pis-tol by his side, h' m, h' m.
Gave a knock and gave a call, h' m, h' m.

3. Said he, "Miss Mouse, are you within?"
   "Yes, kind sir, I sit and spin."

4. He took Miss Mouse upon his knee,
   And said, "Miss Mouse, will you marry me?"

5. "Oh, not without Uncle Rat's consent
   Would I marry the President."

6. Uncle Rat laughed till he shook his side,
   To think his niece would be a bride.

7. "Oh, where will the wedding supper be?"
   "Yonder by that old oak tree."

8. "Oh, what will the wedding supper be?"
   "Two white beans and a black-eyed pea."

9. The first to come was a little moth
   To spread and lay the tablecloth.

10. The next to come was a bumblebee,
    Bow and fiddle on his knee.

11. The third to come was a nimble flea
    To dance a jig with the bumblebee.

12. The fourth to come was a small green fly,
    He ate up all the wedding pie.

13. And fifth to come was a little chick,
    He ate so much it made him sick.

14. At last there came an old tomcat,
    He ate Miss Mouse and Uncle Rat.

15. The frog he jumped into the lake,
    Was swallowed by a big black snake.

16. So here is the end of one, two, three,
    Frog and mouse and bumblebee.

The song has many different versions. This is the version sung by Mary Catherine Moore of Algood, Tennessee.

Shake That Little Foot

Traditional
Briskly

ROTE

American Ballad

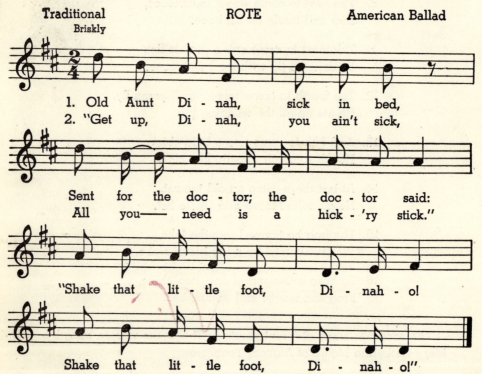

1. Old Aunt Di - nah, sick in bed,
2. "Get up, Di - nah, you ain't sick,

Sent for the doc - tor; the doc - tor said:
All you—— need is a hick - 'ry stick."

"Shake that lit - tle foot, Di - nah - o!

Shake that lit - tle foot, Di - nah - o!"

3. "Sift that meal and save the bran!
   Give it to Dinah to make her stand!" etc.

4. Old Aunt Dinah went to town
   Riding a billy goat, leading a hound, etc.

5. Hound dog barked and billy goat jumped,
   Set Aunt Dinah a-straddle a stump, etc.

Slumber Song

Translated   ROTE   Chilean Lullaby

Smoothly

1. Go to sleep, my ba - by, What shall Moth - er do?
2. La - dy San - ta An - na, Why does Ba - by cry?
3. Go then to my cot - tage, I will give you two;

Wash your lit - tle blan - ket, Make a dress for you.
She has lost her ap - ple, There are none near by.
One for lit - tle Ba - by, Oth - er one for you.

The Spanish name for this song is "Canción de Cuna." The children in Chile sing these words:

1. Duérmete, mi niño,
   ¿Qué tengo que hacer?
   Lavar las mantillas,
   Sentarme a coser.

2. Señora Santa Ana,
   ¿Por qué llora el niño?
   Por una manzana
   Que se ha perdido.

3. ¡Vaya pa' mi casa!
   Y le daré dos.
   Una para el niño,
   Y otra para vos.

(15)

Rosina

Translated   ROTE   French Singing Game

Happily

Good day, hap-py Ro-si-na! In, out, al-ways so gay;
Tell us, what you are do-ing, Here, there, bus-y all day.

I have been play-ing at farm-ing to-day,

Roll-ing in clo-ver, O-ver and o-ver,

I have been play-ing at farm-ing to-day,

Play-ing at farm-ing, That's why I'm gay.

This old European dance, the farandole, is much like the game "Follow the Leader." Boys and girls join hands alternately in a line. In France, they wind in and out of houses and go through the streets, the woods, and the fields. They finally end up in the village square, where they dance in couples.

You can dance the farandole by winding up and down the aisles and around the room. Then with your partner you can make up your own dance.

The Tower on Guard

Translated ROTE Uruguayan Singing Game

Vigorously

Soldiers: 1-3. O cas - tle tow'r, O tow'r on guard!

We're march - ing on your gate.————
Our guns are at your door.————
Your walls are tum - bling down.————

Tower: I'm not a - fraid of you or your sol - diers,
I'm not a - fraid of you or your sol - diers,
Well, then come in, both you and your sol - diers,

You're march - ing here too late.————
You've been here oft be - fore.————
And cap - ture all the town.————

When the children of Uruguay play "La Torre en Guardia" they sing these Spanish words:

Soldiers: ¡La torre en guardia!
　　　　　 ¡La torre en guardia!
　　　　　 La vengo a destruir.

Tower: ¡Pues, yo no temo!
　　　　 ¡Pues, yo no temo!
　　　　 Ni a ti, ni a tus soldados.

The tower is made by two children who grasp each other's hands tightly. Other children form a line of soldiers. The first soldier of the line tries to break down the gate by throwing himself over the arms of the tower. If he fails, the soldiers form a line again and the second soldier tries. If he succeeds, he becomes part of the tower, the line forms again, and the game goes on.

Autumn

Isabel Innes   NOTE   Beth Chaney

Steadily

1. Su - mac leaves are turn - ing red,
2. Sum - mer green is fad - ing brown,

Birds in flight are call - ing;
Flow'rs are dis - ap - pear - ing;

Ap - ples, ri - pened o - ver - head,
Nuts and a - corns rat - tle down,

One by one are fall - ing.
Har - vest time is near - ing.

Below are three rhythm patterns. Chant each one four times.

(1) walk, walk, walk, walk   (2) walk, walk, slow   (3) slow, slow

A walking note (♩) is called a quarter note.

A slow note (♩) is called a half note.

Sunset

K. Stoll   NOTE   Austrian Folk Song

Lit - tle broth - er, now the sun - beams

Hide be - hind the west - ern hill;

All the trees and flow'rs are sleep - ing,

All the for - est birds are still.

When the meter signature is $\frac{4}{4}$ there are four beats to each measure.

Below are two rhythm patterns with the beat under the patterns.

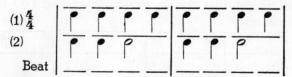

(1) $\frac{4}{4}$
(2)
Beat

How many beats does a quarter note receive?
How many beats does a half note receive?

(21)

The Moon

H. Hinga   NOTE   H. Hinga

Have you seen the moon pass by,

Through the cloud - land gleam - ing?

Drift - ing slow - ly through the sky,

Like a lan - tern beam - ing.

When the meter signature is $\frac{3}{4}$ there are three beats to each measure.

Chant, clap, or step the rhythm pattern, accenting (∧) the first beat in each measure.

The new note is called a dotted half note.

How many beats does it receive?

King Rooster

Translated   ROTE   Latvian Folk Song

Brightly

1. I'm the King of Chick-en Run-way, Cock, cock - a - doo!
2. You will nev - er find me shirk-ing, Cock, cock - a - doo!

Ev - 'ry work-ing day and Sun-day, Cock, cock - a - doo!
Guard-ing chick-ens when they're work-ing, Cock, cock - a - doo!

My sub - jects toil in the gar - den patch,
I chase them out with the ris - ing sun,

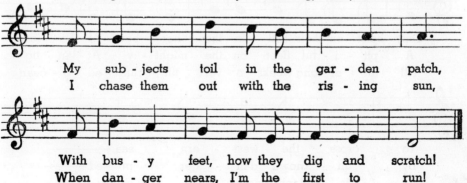

With bus - y feet, how they dig and scratch!
When dan - ger nears, I'm the first to run!

Fourteen Ninety-two

B. Peters   NOTE   B. Peters

1-3. The Ni - ña, the Pin - ta, the San - ta Ma - rí - a

Were sail - ing ves - sels three;——
Sailed on - ward to the west;——
Kept sail - ing day and night;——

They hoist - ed their sail in the har - bor of Pa - los
A pit - i - ful fleet on the might - y At - lan - tic
Till aft - er long weeks o - ver un - chart - ed o - cean

To cross the west - ern sea;——
By un - known dan - ger pressed;——
An is - land came in sight;——

Co - lum - bus was their cap - tain bold,
"Turn back!" the sail - ors urged and pled,
And soon there stood on new - found land,

His men a mot - ley crew,———
Though fair the breez - es blew,———
All per - il safe - ly through,———

Their voy - age old a sto - ry told
"Full sail a - head!" Co - lum - bus said
Co - lum - bus and his fa - mous band

In four - teen nine - ty - two.———

The Goat Kid

Translated NOTE Russian Folk Song

Not too fast

1. Grand-moth-er once had a lit - tle gray goat kid.
2. Grand-moth-er cher-ished her lit - tle gray goat kid.

Vot - kak, vot - kak! Had a gray goat kid.
Vot - kak, vot - kak! Cher-ished her goat kid.

1-6. Vot - kak, vot - kak! Yes, sir, she did!

3. Out for a walk through the wood went the goat kid.
   Votkak, votkak! Out went the goat kid.

4. Quickly a timber wolf fell on the goat kid.
   Votkak, votkak! Fell on the goat kid.

5. Bawling for help ran the little gray goat kid.
   Votkak, votkak! Ran the gray goat kid.

6. Grandmother rescued her little gray goat kid.
   Votkak, votkak! Rescued her goat kid.

Votkak means "That's how it is" or "That's so."

There are quarter rests in this song.

(26)

Market Day

Adapted
Briskly

NOTE

French Folk Song

1. Come, get up! The clock is ring - ing,
2. Dew - drops shin - ing, blue - birds sing - ing,

Soon the sun will raise its head;
Bright - en all the coun - try - side;

This is Mar - ket Day, re - mem - ber,
Pack the cab - bage in the wag - on,

That's no time to stay in bed!
Climb on top and take a ride!

When the meter signature is $\frac{2}{4}$ there are two beats in each measure.

$\frac{2}{4}$
Beat | — — | — — | — — | — — | — — |

Below are two rhythm patterns.

(1) $\frac{2}{4}$
(2)
Beat ∧ — — | ∧ — — | ∧ — — | ∧ — — |

Running notes are called eighth notes.
How many eighth notes equal one beat?

(27)

The Green Bus

James Tippett   NOTE   Charles Crane

Wait a min-ute, green bus,   slow down,   stop!

I will climb your wind-ing stair and   ride   on   top.

A - long the bus - y   riv - er, down the   av - e - nue,

Most an - y day I   like   to take   a   trip with   you.

There are eighth rests in this song. ♪ ♪

(28)

Daydreaming

J. W. Beattie

NOTE

Old Tune

Not too fast

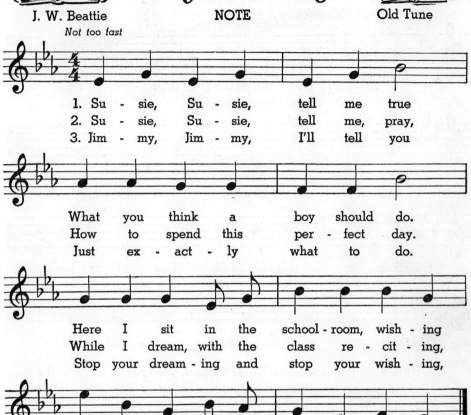

1. Su - sie, Su - sie, tell me true
2. Su - sie, Su - sie, tell me, pray,
3. Jim - my, Jim - my, I'll tell you

What you think a boy should do.
How to spend this per - fect day.
Just ex - act - ly what to do.

Here I sit in the school - room, wish - ing
While I dream, with the class re - cit - ing,
Stop your dream - ing and stop your wish - ing,

I could be by the mill - pond fish - ing.
All the bass in the lake are bit - ing.
Do your school - work and then go fish - ing.

Tidy-o

Traditional   NOTE   Missouri Version

Brightly

A. Pass one win - dow, ti - dy - o,
   Pass three win - dows, ti - dy - o,

Pass two win - dows, ti - dy - o,
Pass four win - dows, ti - dy - o.

B. Skip to the cen - ter and bow to your beau,

All come a - jing - ling, ti - dy - o.

A. Form a single circle. Join hands to make windows. A child in the center passes in and out the windows.

B. The child skips to the center and bows to a child in the circle. All move around the circle on "All come a-jingling, tidy-o." On the repeat, all move to the center and back and around the circle.

The signs 𝄆   𝄇 mean "Repeat the music between these signs."

The Bridge of Avignon

Translated   **NOTE**   French Singing Game

Gaily

On the bridge near the town Folks are danc-ing, gai-ly danc-ing,
Sur le pont d'A-vi-gnon L'on y dan-se, l'on y dan-se,

On the bridge near the town, On the bridge of A-vi-gnon.
Sur le pont d'A-vi-gnon L'on y dan-se tout en rond.

All the men bow this way,   Then a-gain bow that way.
La-dies curt-sy this way,   Turn and curt-sy that way.
Beaux mes-sieurs font comm' çi,   Et puis en-core comm' ça.
Les belles dames font comm' çi,   Et puis en-core comm' ça.

When French children play this game, they make up all kinds of things to do with the last line, such as "Little birds fly this way," "Babies all cry this way," "Parrots chatter this way." They call the song "Sur le pont d'Avignon."

(31)

The New Hat

M. C. Cherryman   NOTE   French Folk Song

Not too fast

1. I met a fair and love - ly maid
2. "Well, my um - brel - la's quite a help,"

Up - on a Mon - day morn;
I an - swered, "in a show'r."

I smiled at her but, sad to say,
And then she turned her pret - ty face,

She turned a - way with scorn.
So like a gar - den flow'r.

It was a rath - er cloud - y day,
"Then come and walk with me," she said,

She   wore   a   dain - ty   hat;
"And   shield   my   brand - new   hat."

I   said, "I'm   sure   it's   going   to   rain."
"But   I   must   hold   your   arm,"   I   said.

She   an - swered, "What   of   that?"
She   an - swered, "What   of   that?"

This song starts on the fourth beat of the measure. Accent the beat after each bar.

Find the third below <u>fa</u>. Sing it; build it.

(33)

Mandandiran

Translated   NOTE   Chilean Singing Game

Brightly

1. Boys: O good morn - ing, La - dy Slaugh - ter,
   Girls: I'll con - sid - er, Mis - ter Ro - sen,

Man - dan - dir - an, dir - an, dan.

I should like to wed your daugh - ter,
If you tell me which you've cho - sen,

Man - dan - dir - an, dir - an, dan.

2. Boys: I have chosen Margarita,
   With a fine new name I'll greet her.
   Girls: Then what fine new name to greet her
   Will you give to Margarita?

3. Boys: I've a charming name to give her,
   I shall call her Chicken Liver.
   Girls: What a funny kind of name, sir,
   Such a name would only shame her.

(34)

4. **Boys:** Then I'll call her Sweet Rosita,
   In exchange for Margarita.
   Girls: "You may wed my little daughter,"
   Said the noble Lady Slaughter.

This song starts on the second beat.

Marching Scouts

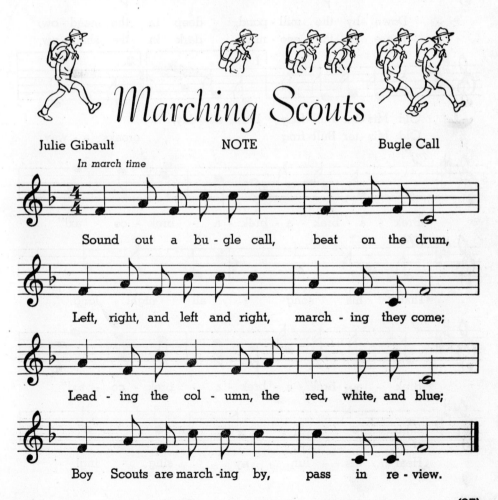

Julie Gibault   NOTE   Bugle Call

In march time

Sound out a bu - gle call, beat on the drum,

Left, right, and left and right, march - ing they come;

Lead - ing the col - umn, the red, white, and blue;

Boy Scouts are march -ing by, pass in re - view.

(35)

Mr. Bullfrog

J. W. Beattie   ROTE   Rubén Carámbula

Moderately fast

Down by the mill-pond, deep in the mead-ow,
There in the eve-ning, dark in the shad-ow,

Old Mis-ter Bull-frog hides all day;
Old Mis-ter Bull-frog croaks a-way.

"Brek - a - brek - a - brek - a - brek - co - ax!"

That's his song all night long.

"Brek - a - brek - a - brek - a - brek - co - ax!"

Hear his fun - ny sing - ing!

Hey, Mis-ter Bull-frog! Say, Mis-ter Bull-frog!
Hey, Mis-ter Bull-frog! Say, Mis-ter Bull-frog!

1. Where did you ev-er learn that song?
2. Some-bod-y must have taught you wrong!

Divide the class. One group sings the words while the second group makes a rhythmic accompaniment by imitating the sounds of frogs.

My Pony

Charles Crane   NOTE   Charles Crane

1. My po-ny, old Jim, runs up when I call,
2. In sum-mer we ride thro' woods green and cool,
3. In win-ter old Jim stays safe-ly at home,

We gal-lop to school in the spring and fall.
When thirs-ty, we drink from a spar-kling pool.
I climb on the bus and then go a-lone.

On which beat does this song start? Find the third below la. Sing it; build it.

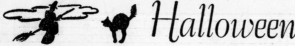

Halloween

J. W. Beattie   ROTE   Mary Thom

Mysteriously

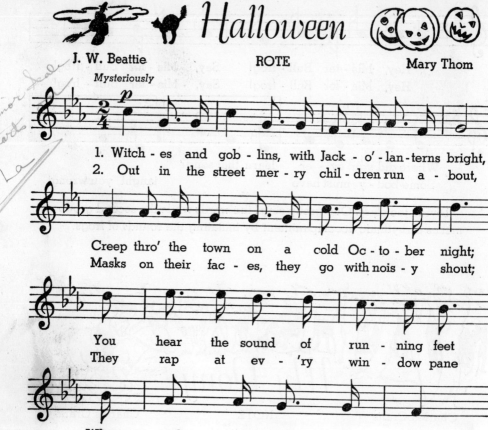

1. Witch - es and gob - lins, with Jack - o' - lan - terns bright,
2. Out in the street mer - ry chil - dren run a - bout,

Creep thro' the town on a cold Oc - to - ber night;
Masks on their fac - es, they go with nois - y shout;

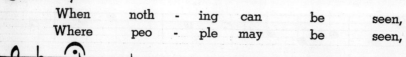

You hear the sound of run - ning feet
They rap at ev - 'ry win - dow pane

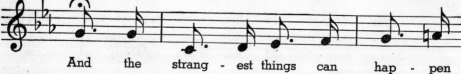

When noth - ing can be seen,
Where peo - ple may be seen,

And the strang - est things can hap - pen

On a wild—— Hal - low - een!——

Prayer for Peace

Isabel Innes   NOTE   Welsh Hymn Tune

Reverently

Thou, the Al - might - y   Rul - er   of   cre - a - tion,

Mak - er   of   moun - tain,   val - ley,   sea,   and   plain,

Lead   us,   Thy   chil - dren,   ev-'ry   race   and   na - tion,

That   all   the   world   may   live   in   peace   a - gain.

$\frac{4}{4}$
Beat

The new note is called a whole note. How many beats does it receive?

(39)

Can You Play?

Translated   ROTE   French Singing Game

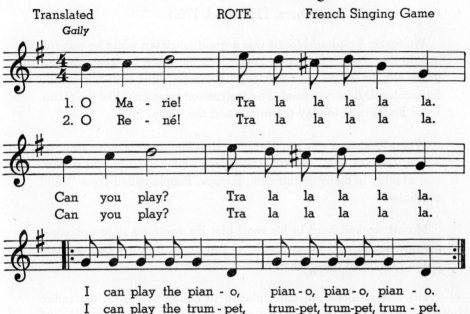

1. O Ma - rie!   Tra la la la la la.
2. O Re - né!   Tra la la la la la.

Can you play?   Tra la la la la la.
Can you play?   Tra la la la la la.

I can play the pian - o,   pian - o, pian - o, pian - o.
I can play the trum - pet,   trum-pet, trum-pet, trum - pet.

You can play a real or a make-believe instrument. Sing the song to someone in your class, asking him to play. He will answer you. After each instrument is introduced, the other players repeat their solos in the order in which they joined in. At the end, all the children sing, "We can play together, together, together."

There are four choirs of instruments in the orchestra.

> Violin and cello belong to the String Choir.
> Clarinet and flute belong to the Wood-wind Choir.
> Trumpet and trombone belong to the Brass Choir.
> Drums and tambourine belong to the Percussion Choir.

Can you name other instruments in each choir?

Wolfgang Amadeus Mozart

(born, 1756; died, 1791)

Wolfgang Amadeus Mozart was a great musician while he was still a little boy. Before he began music lessons, when he was only four years old, he could play and even compose short melodies on the harpsichord. A harpsichord is an instrument somewhat like the piano. Later he learned to play the organ and the violin.

When Wolfgang was six, his father took him and his older sister on a long concert tour. The children played for the kings and queens and nobility in many countries in Europe. People called them "child prodigies."

Mozart worked hard in his short life. He wrote many symphonies, operas, songs, and other pieces of music. In time he became one of the best-loved musicians in the whole world.

His compositions are often played in concerts and on the radio. If you listen to orchestra music on the radio, you surely have heard many of them. You will find some of the lovely melodies he wrote on the next pages. Words have been written for them, so that you can sing them.

Music Magic

Adapted   ROTE   Mozart

Smoothly

O - ver the air soft mu - sic is wing - ing,

Tones of far - off voic - es come sing - ing,

Fill - ing my heart, sweet mag - ic they're bring - ing

On the wings of mel - o - dy.

Mozart wrote this melody in his Piano Sonata in A Major.

(43)

Autumn Comes

Adapted

NOTE

Mozart

Smoothly

1. Au - tumn comes with her har - vest,
2. Fruit and grain must be gath - ered

With her bright crim - son leaves,—
For the cold days to come,—

With her grapes glow - ing pur - ple
Thro' the warm au - tumn sun - light

And her shin - ing gold - en sheaves.
Let us bring the har - vest home.

What is the third above re? What is the third above fa? The three notes make the chord re-fa-la. Sing and build the two chord figures in the tonal pattern.

A Wood-wind Duet

Adapted — ROTE — Mozart

In strict time

1. Hear the ech - o - ing tones of flute and clar - i -
play - ing a tune you nev - er can for -

Tones of flute and clar - i - net.
Tune you nev - er can for - get.

net, As they an - swer each
get, Made by Mo - zart just

They are play-ing a du - et.
For the flute and clar - i - net.

oth-er play-ing a du - et.
for the flute and clar - i - net.

2. Hear them

This little dialogue between flute and clarinet starts the trio of the minuet from Mozart's Symphony in E-flat Major. The instruments play notes an octave higher than they are given here.

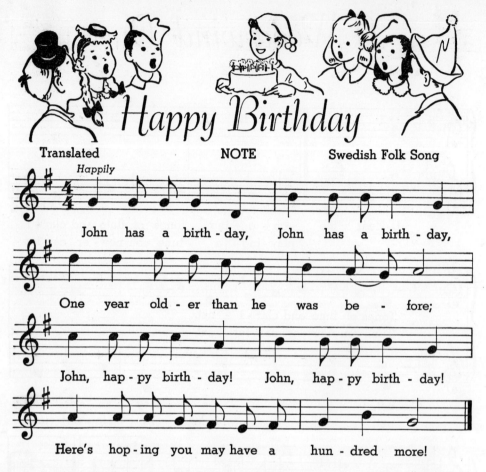

Happy Birthday

Translated   NOTE   Swedish Folk Song

Happily

John has a birth-day, John has a birth-day,

One year old-er than he was be-fore;

John, hap-py birth-day! John, hap-py birth-day!

Here's hop-ing you may have a hun-dred more!

The name of anyone who has a birthday may be used. What kind of notes would you use if you were singing to Edward or Mary?

A Nick and a Nock

Translated   ROTE   Swedish Singing Game

In strict time

A. Jump to the swing of a live-ly tune,

(46)

With a   nick and a   nock and a   one, two,   three.

Hand   to your   part - ner, now   twist a - bout,

End

With a   nick   and a   nock, two,   three.———

B. With a   hop, hop, hop,   and a   clop, clop, clop,

Go back to sign 𝄋

Move a - round the   room,   two,—   three.———   Give your

Partners face each other with hands joined.

A. **Bleking Step.** Both jump, placing their right heels forward and thrusting their right arms forward with elbows straight, so that their bodies are twisted to the left. Both jump again, using the left heel and left arm. They jump three more quick jumps to complete the bleking.

B. **Hopsa Step.** Couples face, with their hands joined and extended sideward. The boy hops twice on his left foot, while the girl hops twice on her right foot. The free foot is raised high to the side. Both alternate left and right or right and left. The couples circle around the room as they do the hopsa step.

Father Noah

Translated   NOTE   Swedish Folk Song

Briskly

1-3. Fa-ther No-ah, Fa-ther No-ah was a fa-mous man!

Built a ves-sel snug and trim be - fore the flood be - gan;
Sailed with ze -bra, pol - ar bear, and wild o - rang - u - tan.
Land -ed on a moun-tain top with-out a sin - gle plan;

An - i - mals of ev-'ry kind crowd-ed quar-ters did not mind,
Bea-ver, skunk, and por-cu-pine found the jour-ney ver - y fine,
Led the crea-tures from the ark, plant - ed trees, and made a park,

Fol-lowed No - ah to his boat and off they went a - float.
Kept from ar - gu - ments and fights for man - y days and nights.
Set - tled down to work a - gain be - neath a rain-bow's end.

This is one of the best-known folk songs of Sweden. There are many
verses, all having to do with the Biblical story of Noah and the ark.

Spinning Song

Translated   ROTE   Norwegian Folk Song

Moderately fast

Near the fire - side, burn - ing bright - ly,

Moth - er's wheel is turn - ing night - ly,

Pleas - ant thoughts to chil - dren bring - ing,

Hap - py voic - es laugh and sing.

Sing a song, fa la ra la ra la,

Sing a song, fa la ra la ra.

Row Your Boat

Traditional　　　　　　　ROTE　　　　　American Round

Row, row,　row your boat Gen-tly down the　stream,—

Mer - ri - ly,　mer - ri - ly,　　mer - ri - ly, mer - ri - ly,

Life　　is　　but　　a　　dream.———

Divide the class into two sections. Section One sings the first phrase alone. When it starts the second phrase, Section Two begins singing the first phrase. Each section sings the entire song two or three times.

My Shadow and I

Daniel Protheroe　　　　　　ROTE　　　　　Daniel Protheroe

Not too fast

1. Come　　dance,　　my　　lit - tle　　shad - ow,
2. When　　days　　are　　gray　and　　cloud - y,

(50)

And   I   will dance with   you;
He's   sure   to   hide a -   way,

Come   run,   my lit - tle shad - ow,
Al - though I al - ways call him

And   I   will scam - per   too;
To   hur - ry out   and   play;

When the   day   is sun - ny, bright and clear,
But if   I could find the shad - ow house,

As   soon   as   I   go   out,
Wher - ev - er it may   be,

I   al - ways find my shad - ow wait - ing
I'd put my arms a - round my shad - ow

To   fol - low me   a -   bout.
And bring him home with   me.

(51)

Are You Sleeping?

Translated   NOTE   French Round

Are you sleep-ing,   are you sleep-ing,
Frè-re Jac-ques,   Frè-re Jac-ques,

Broth-er John,   Broth-er John?
Dor-mez-vous,   dor-mez-vous?

Morn-ing bells are ring-ing,   morn-ing bells are ring-ing,
Son-nez les ma-ti-nes,   son-nez les ma-ti-nes,

Ding ding dong!   Ding ding dong!
Din dan don!   Din dan don!

Do

A Prayer

Adapted   NOTE   Gregorian Chant

Reverently

God, the Fa - ther, hear our plea,

Grant us Thy bless - ing ev - 'ry day;

Help us serve and hon - or Thee,

Guide ev - 'ry foot - step, show the way.

Sing and build the key chord. The key chord is also called the tonic chord. The curved line joining two different notes is called a slur.

The Ship

Adapted   **NOTE**   Breton Folk Song

In strict time

1. See the   ship   in   the   har - bor   ly - ing,
2. Helms-man strong holds the   rud - der   stead - y,

Soon   to   sail   for   a   dis - tant   sea;
Men   on   deck   make   the   rig - ging   fast;

O - ver - head,   pen - nants bright   are   fly - ing,
Now   on   board   ev - 'ry - thing   is   read - y,

Peo - ple   wave   from   the   bus - y   quay.
An - chor   up,   there   she   goes   at   last!

This song starts on the third beat.

Clap or step the beat. Clap or step the rhythm pattern. Accent the
beat after each bar.

(54)

Sea Shell

Amy Lowell
(adapted)

ROTE

J. Wolverton

Smoothly, slowly

p

Sea shell, sea shell, sing me a song, O please,—

A song— of ships and sail - or men,

mf

And par - rots and trop - i - cal trees;——

p

Of fish - es and cor - als un - der the waves,

slower

And sea hors - es sta - bled in great— green caves,—

p in time   *pp*

Sea shell, sea shell, sing me a song, O please!—

(55)

Little Night Wind

Translated   NOTE   Carl Spezier

Smoothly, slowly

1. Lit - tle night wind, sigh - ing,
2. Lit - tle moon - beam, stray - ing,

Hush my ba - by, cry - ing,
Round his pil - low play - ing,

Soothe him with thy dream - y charm,
As you dim your sil - ver beam,

Let no breath of fear a - larm,
Un - der - neath the star - light gleam,

Wind, gen - tly sigh - ing,
Far from him stray - ing,

Keep him   safe   from   harm!
Leave   a   gold - en   dream!

Build the key chord, or tonic chord. Find the third above <u>la</u>. Sing it;
build it. There are many slurs in this song.

Early Frost

Isabel Innes   ROTE   Old Tune
Lightly

1. One   time   in   Oc - to - ber, when   all were in bed,
2. Next   morn - ing the gar - den was   with-ered and bare,

Jack   Frost   went a - bout   in   the   night;———
The   scent   of   the   ros - es   was   lost;———

He   paint - ed   the   ma - ple leaves   or - ange and red,
Ripe   wal - nuts and chest - nuts were   flung here and there,

The   grass   with   a   car - pet   of   white.———
Be - cause   of   that   call from Jack   Frost.———

Dream Rhymes

Lloyd Norlin

NOTE

Lloyd Norlin

In waltz time

1. Late in the night when I lie in my bed,
2. Soon I grow drow-sy and sleep comes at last,

Odd lit-tle sounds go a-round in my head;
Ev-'ry com-pan-ion is still go-ing past;

Sleep will not come, so I make up a game,
None dis-ap-pears and quite of-ten, it seems,

Rhym-ing my friends and my play-mates by name.
All of us play thro' the night in my dreams.

Chorus

ROTE

Ed-die, Ted-dy, Fred-dy, and Jim,

Mar - y, Ger - ry, Har - ry, and Tim,

John - ny, Con - nie, Bon - nie, and Sue,

They are my play-mates in school.——

Repeat, singing the names of your playmates.

The Swing

1. How do you like to go up in a swing,
   Up in the air so blue?
   Oh, I do think it the pleasantest thing
   Ever a child can do!

2. Up in the air and over the wall
   Till I can see so wide,
   Rivers and trees and cattle and all
   Over the countryside—

3. Till I look down on the garden green,
   Down on the roof so brown—
   Up in the air I go flying again,
   Up in the air and down.

Can you make your own tune for "The Swing"? The poem was written by Robert Louis Stevenson. Chant the words a few times. Then sing them to your own melody.

(59)

The Traveler

Jeannette Gordon   NOTE   Grace V. Wilson

Brightly

1. I gath - ered my be - long - ings
2. I saw the sights in Rus - sia,
3. The folk in far - off coun - tries,

In - to a trav - 'ler's pack,
In Swe - den and in Rome,
Who seemed at first quite queer,

And start - ed off to jour - ney
And stayed a while in Chi - na
Be - came, when once I knew them,

A - round the world and back.
Be - fore I start - ed home.
Just like the peo - ple here.

The song starts on the last part of the second beat.

Beat

The Contrary Owl

Adapted   NOTE   Silesian Folk Song

Brightly

1. I met an owl one aft - er - noon;
2. Said I, "You're in a fun - ny plight
3. The les - son of this tale is plain,

Said he, "Your bed - time's com - ing soon,
To have to fly and work at night."
But yet I al - ways will main - tain

And while you snug - gle warm in bed
Said he, "It's just the oth - er way,
Al - tho' an owl sees best at night,

I'll fly a - round and work in - stead."
You're fun - ny when you work by day."
He looks much bet - ter in the light.

Bubble Pipe Dream

Virginia Murdock   NOTE   Mary Thom

Gaily

1. I have a bub - ble pipe at home,
2. I'll pass the Dip - pers, big and small,

And on a sun - ny day
And skirt the Ple - ia - des,

I'll blow a bub - ble large e - nough
On Ju - pi - ter and Sat - urn call

To car - ry me a - way;
Po - lite - ly as you please;

I'll soar in - to the stra - to - sphere,
I'll touch O - ri - on's belt and sword,

A - bove the clouds to ride,
Go sail - ing by the moon,

And vis - it plan - ets far and near,
But when I'm hun - gry I'll be sure

With stars on ev - 'ry side.
To float on home at noon.

How many eighth rests can you find?

Sliding

Adapted   ROTE

Philip Hayes
(Round)

1   2

Slid - ing a - long, we skim o'er the snow,

And we sing a song as on we go.

(63)

Harvest Time

Our early settlers enjoyed getting together for parties in the fall, when the summer work was over and the crops had been gathered. At these parties they liked to sing, dance, and play games.

There were four favorite ways of dancing: (1) in a circle; (2) in a square of four couples; (3) in two lines, with partners facing; and (4) in separate couples.

Calls were shouted to keep the couples together. Sometimes these calls were sung. Perhaps someone in your class would like to call while the rest of you dance. Here are some of the calls which are used:

"Circle to the right!"
> Circle moves to the right.

"Circle to the left!"
> Circle moves to the left.

"Promenade!"
> Couples walk around the circle with their hands joined in a double handshake.

"Sashay!"
> Partners face, join hands, and slide sideward.

"Swing!"
> Partners face, join hands, stand so that their right sides almost touch, and pivot around in place.

"Grand right and left!"
> Partners face and shake right hands. Each person then moves forward and gives his left hand and right hand alternately to the persons he meets. All continue around the circle.

Old Brass Wagon

Traditional   ROTE   American Singing Game

Vigorously

1. Cir - cle to the left, the Old Brass Wag - on,
2. Swing,— O— swing, the Old Brass Wag - on,

Cir - cle to the left, the Old Brass Wag - on,
Swing,— O— swing, the Old Brass Wag - on,

Cir - cle to the left, the Old Brass Wag - on,
Swing,— O— swing, the Old Brass Wag - on,

You're the one, my dar - ling.
You're the one, my dar - ling.

3. Promenade home, the Old Brass Wagon, etc.

4. Sashay in and out, the Old Brass Wagon, etc.

5. Break and swing, the Old Brass Wagon, etc.

6. Promenade around the Old Brass Wagon, etc.

Choose partners and form a single circle, with the girl to the right of the boy. Then do what the song tells you to do.

Caller's Song

Traditional
Brightly

ROTE

American Singing Game

The end two gents cross o - ver and by the la - dies stand,

The side two gents cross o - ver and we all join hands,

You bow to the cor - ner la - dy, you bow to your part-ners all,

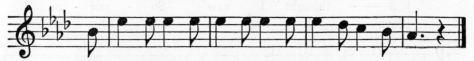

You swing the cor-ner la - dy and you prom-e-nade the hall.

Form a square of four couples, with the girl to the right of the boy. The couples in the square are numbered 1, 2, 3, and 4. The first and third couples are the "end couples." The "corner lady" is the lady at the left of each boy. The song tells you what to do.

Sing the entire song a second time for the promenade, so that the couples can circle twice. The girl leads her new partner back to her place in the square. Repeat the game until the original partners are back together again.

Oh! Susanna

Stephen Foster   ROTE   Stephen Foster

Briskly

1. { Oh, I come from Al - a - bam - a
   { It rained all night the day I
2. { I had a dream the oth - er
   { The buck - wheat cake was in her

{ With my ban - jo on my knee,
{ left, The weath - er it was dry,
{ night When ev - 'ry - thing was still,
{ mouth, The tear was in her eye,

{ I'm goin' to Lou' - si - an - a,
{ The sun so hot I froze to
{ I thought I saw Su - san - a
{ Says I, "I'm com - ing from the

1.   2.

{ My true love for to see.
{ death, Su - san - a, don't you cry.
{ A com - ing down the hill.
{ south, Su - san - a, don't you cry."

Oh! Su - san - na, oh, don't you cry for me,

For I come from Al - a - bam - a

With my ban - jo on my knee.

Choose partners and form a single circle, with the girl to the right of the boy. The girls move to the center and back during the first phrase. The boys move to the center and back during the second phrase. On the repeat, partners face each other and the whole circle does the "Grand right and left" until the chorus. For the chorus, each person swings with the person whose hand he has at the time the chorus begins. If you like, vary the dance with different calls.

Pop! Goes the Weasel

Traditional   ROTE   American Folk Song

Lively

1. — All a-round the chicken coop
2. A penny for a spool— of thread,
3. First couple lead right out to the right

The monkey chased the weasel,
A penny for a needle,
And balance there so easy,

That's the way the money goes,
That's the way the money goes,
Three join hands and circle left,

1-3. Pop! goes the weasel.

I've no time to wait— and sigh,

No   time   to   whee - dle;

On - ly time   to   say   good - by,

Pop!   goes   the   wea - sel.

Trucks

1. Big trucks for steel beams,
   Big trucks for coal,
   Rumbling down the broad streets,
   Heavily they roll.

2. Little trucks for groceries,
   Little trucks for bread,
   Turning into every street,
   Rushing on ahead.

3. Big trucks, little trucks,
   In never-ending lines,
   Rumble on and rush ahead
   While I read the signs.

This poem, by James S. Tippett, can be made into an interesting song. Try to make up a melody for it.

Telling Time

Marie W. Clark   ROTE   Marie W. Clark

1. I wake at sev - en ev - 'ry day,
2. In Lon - don town, the chil - dren hear

My break - fast is just at eight,————
A fa - mous re - sound - ing chime,————

And ver - y - soon I leave for school
They know Big Ben is call - ing them

So I shall not be late;————
To tell them of the time;————

I of - ten think of boys and girls
In Spain and France and It - a - ly,

Who live a - cross the sea,————
From tall ca - the - dral tow'rs,————

And all the clocks that speak to them,
The gold - en tones of bells are heard,

Just as my clock tells me.
Ring - ing the pass - ing hours.

Scotland's Burning

Traditional   NOTE   American Round

Scot - land's burn - ing, Scot - land's burn - ing,

Fetch the en - gine, Fetch the en - gine,

Fire! Fire! Fire! Fire! Pour on wa - ter, Pour on wa - ter.

Swedish Lullaby

Adapted   ROTE—NOTE   Swedish Folk Song

1. Hush, hush! High in the tree, Green your cra-dle is swing-ing;
2. Hush, hush! Moth-er is near, Soft-ly breez-es are sigh-ing;

Lull - a - by,   hear your   moth - er   sing - ing,
Go   to   sleep   now and   hush   your   cry - ing,

Hush, lit - tle ba - by,   Lull - a,   lull - a - by.
Hush, lit - tle ba - by,   Lull - a,   lull - a - by.

After you know the song with words, sing the last phrase with syllables. What is the last syllable?

When a song ends on <u>la,</u> it is a minor song. When a song ends on <u>do,</u> it is a major song.

Sad Mother Nature

J. W. Beattie   NOTE   J. Wolverton

Slowly

1. Moth - er Na - ture is wear - ing a frown,
2. Moth - er Na - ture, be hap - py, please do!

She moans and sighs all day;———
Your friends don't go to stay;———

Her friends of sum - mer are turn - ing to brown
They take va - ca - tions the long win - ter thro',

And soon they'll be go - ing a - way.———
You'll see them next A - pril or May.———

Sing and build the tonal patterns. Why is this a minor song?

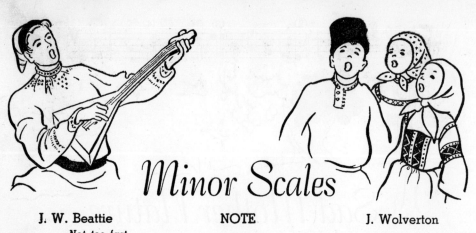

Minor Scales

J. W. Beattie   NOTE   J. Wolverton

Not too fast

1. If you are a tune de - tec - tor
2. Peo - ple in the north - ern coun - tries
3. La ti do re mi la sol fa,

Look - ing aft - er small de - tails,
Where the mid - night sun pre - vails,
In - di - ans, Chi - nese, or Gaels,

You will see how mu - sic mak - ers
Nor - way, Swe - den, Fin - land, Rus - sia,
Make their mu - sic sad or hap - py,

Use the mi - nor scales.
Like the mi - nor scales.
Sing - ing mi - nor scales.

Giving Thanks

Evanston children   ROTE   Evanston children

Firmly

Thank you, God, for love and care; Thank you for the

clothes we wear, Thank you for our homes and food,

You are al - ways kind and good; Thank you for our

strength and health, For our coun - try's har - vest wealth,

Thanks for love and life and joy,

Thanks from ev - 'ry girl and boy.

Thanksgiving Day

Edna Becker   ROTE   Grace V. Wilson

Joyfully

1. There's a turkey in the ice-box,
2. For the aunts and uncles gathered

There are pies upon the shelf,
And my cousins large and small,

There are dough-nuts in the pan-try,
We have made the ta-ble long-er,

But I cannot help my-self;
There is room e-nough for all;

If I step in-to the kitchen,
Father carves the roast-ed turkey

(78)

I will hear some-bod-y say:
And we eat it all some-how,

"You just wait un-til to-mor-row,
Moth-er says: "Clean up the plat-ter!

It will be Thanks-giv-ing Day."
This is glad Thanks-giv-ing now."

Winter Winds

Lloyd Norlin   NOTE   Lloyd Norlin

Slowly

1. Thro' the skies go sail-ing Cold gray storm clouds,
2. Flakes of snow are fall-ing, Cold gray storm clouds,

Win-ter winds are wail-ing, Oo-oo-oo-oo.
Win-ter winds are call-ing, Oo-oo-oo-oo.

You know how to build the major key chord, <u>do-mi-sol-do</u>. Sing and
build the minor key chord. Begin on <u>la</u>.

(79)

Festival of Lights

Translated
(adapted)

ROTE

Folk Song

Brightly

1. Thro' the night win-dows bright shed a friend-ly beam,
2. Thro' the day chil-dren play, laugh and dance and sing,

In a row can-dles glow with their spar-kling gleam;
Par-ents hear, gath-er near, sil-ver pres-ents bring;

Neigh-bors call, one and all, tops go spin-ning round.
Fam-'lies eat pan-cakes sweet, roast-ed duck-ling, prime.

Hum, hum, hum! Drum, drum, drum! Hear the mer-ry sound.
Hum, hum, hum! Drum, drum, drum! What a hap-py time!

The Festival of Lights is an eight-day holiday celebrated in the month of December. Its origin goes back to Old Testament times.

The Angel's Message

Translated   **ROTE**   Rhineland Carol
used by Bach

Slowly

1. From   heav'n on   high   I   come   to   earth
2. To - day   a   ba - by   small   was   born,

To   tell   you   of   the   Sav - iour's birth;
He   came   to   you   this   Christ - mas   morn;

I   bring good   news   and   words   of   cheer
So   hap - py   be   and   loud - ly   sing

For   you   and   ev - 'ry - one that's here.
To   wel - come Christ, the   Heav'n - ly   King.

(81)

Silent Night

Joseph Mohr   ROTE   Franz Gruber
Descant by Ewald Nolte

Smoothly

Loo

Loo

1-3.   Si - lent night!   Ho - ly night!

Loo

Loo

All   is   calm,   all   is   bright
Shep - herds quake   at   the   sight,
Son   of   God,   love's   pure   light

Loo

Round   yon   Vir - gin   Moth - er   and   Child,
Glo - ries   stream—— from   heav'n—— a - far,
Ra - diant   beams   from   Thy   ho - ly   face

Ho - ly In - fant so ten - der and mild,
Heav'n - ly hosts sing al - le - lu - ia,
With the dawn of re - deem - ing grace,

Loo

Sleep in heav - en - ly peace,————
Christ, the Sav - iour, is born,————
Je - sus, Lord, at Thy birth,————

Loo

Sleep—— in heav - en - ly peace.————
Christ,—— the Sav - iour, is born.————
Je - sus, Lord, at Thy birth.————

(83)

Little Pine Tree

J. W. Beattie   ROTE   Russian Folk Song

In moderate time

1. Once a pine brave-ly stood near the edge of a wood,
2. Said a birch tree quite tall to the pine young and small,
3. Then the birch bend-ing low whis-pered, "Sure-ly you know

All a-round it tall birch-es gleam-ing sil-ver-y white;
"With a green dress of sum-mer you're the on-ly one here."
Of the trees in the for-est you're the rich-est to me,

And the pine tree of green from a-far could be seen
Said the pine mourn-ful-ly, "I'm as poor as can be,
For your glad col-or bright is for-ev-er in sight,

Stand-ing there in the snow, its branch-es glim-mer-ing bright.
Hav-ing on-ly one gown, I wear it all thro' the year."
And you bring joy and cheer, my lit-tle green Christ-mas tree."

The Holy Child

Translated   ROTE   Colombian Villancico

Moderately fast

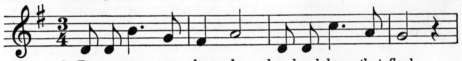

1. For a man - ger low - ly, shep-herds leave their flocks,
2. To a man - ger jour - ney stran-gers from a - far,
3. All the friend - ly chil - dren, Mar - y, sweet and mild,

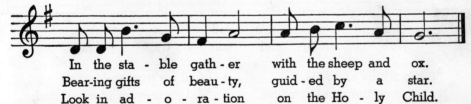

In the sta - ble gath - er with the sheep and ox.
Bear-ing gifts of beau - ty, guid - ed by a star.
Look in ad - o - ra - tion on the Ho - ly Child.

Among the Spanish-speaking neighbors of Latin-American countries, a Christmas song is called a villancico. This villancico is "Vamos Pastorcitos." The children of Colombia sing these Spanish words:

¡Vamos pastorcitos!
¡Vamos a Belén!
A ver a la Virgen
Y al Niño también.

Yule Nisse

Translated   ROTE   Danish Folk Song
Gaily

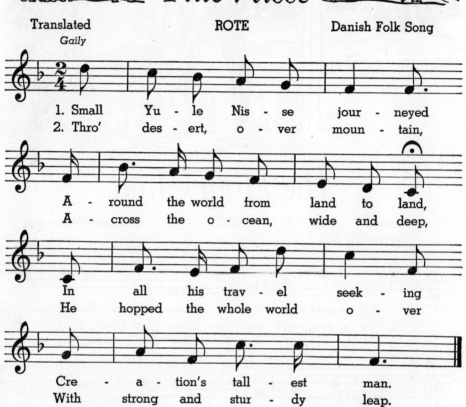

1. Small Yu - le Nis - se jour - neyed
2. Thro' des - ert, o - ver moun - tain,

A - round the world from land to land,
A - cross the o - cean, wide and deep,

In all his trav - el seek - ing
He hopped the whole world o - ver

Cre - a - tion's tall - est man.
With strong and stur - dy leap.

3. To Africa and Asia,
Among the races primitive,
To China, where they told him
The one-eyed giants live.

4. In all his trips and travels,
'Mid journeying of every kind,
He never gave up trying
The tallest man to find.

5. At last, in desperation
He stared into the sea close by,
Said he, in glad elation,
"The tallest man is I!"

Yule Nisse (pronounced yoola nissa) is a dwarf known to all the children of Denmark.

New Year

Adapted   ROTE   Danish Christmas Song

Moderately

Hear the ring - ing stee - ple bell,

Peal - ing forth the year's fare - well,

Slow - ly in the bel - fry swing - ing,

Sad and cheer - ful mem - 'ries bring - ing,

Toll - ing out the dy - ing year,

Toll - ing in a glad New Year!

Locating Do

The teacher has helped you locate the keynote, or <u>do</u>, in your songs. You will be able to do it yourself if you follow these rules:

The <u>sharp</u> farthest to the right in the key signature is called <u>ti</u>. Count down <u>ti sol mi do</u> or <u>ti la sol fa mi re do</u>.

The <u>flat</u> farthest to the right is called <u>fa</u>. Count down to <u>do</u>.

Musical Terms

Often, in reading music, you find signs which use Italian words. You need to know the following:

p—<u>piano</u>	soft	f—<u>forte</u>	loud
mp—<u>mezzo piano</u>	moderately soft	mf—<u>mezzo forte</u>	moderately loud
pp—<u>pianissimo</u>	very soft	ff—<u>fortissimo</u>	very loud

By the Light of the Moon

Translated   NOTE   French Folk Song

1. "Now the moon is shin-ing, My good friend, Pier-rot,
2. In the shin-ing moon-light, Pier-rot soft-ly said,
   "Au clair de la lu-ne, Mon a-mi Pier-rot,
   Au clair de la lu-ne, Pier-rot ré-pon-dit,

Wak-en from your slum-ber, Hear me knock-ing low;
"I've no pen to lend you, And I'm in my bed;
Prê-te moi ta plu-me, Pour é-crire un mot;
"Je n'ai pas de plu-me, Je suis dans mon lit;

I must write a let-ter, Lend your pen to me;
Go next door and ask them, They're at home to-night;
Ma chan-delle est mor-te, Je n'ai plus de feu;
Va chez la voi-si-ne, Je crois qu'elle y est,

Won't you strike a match, please? I can hard-ly see."
In their kit-chen win-dow Lights are burn-ing bright."
Ou-vre moi ta por-te, Pour l'a-mour de Dieu."
Car, dans sa cui-si-ne On bat le bri-quet."

In France this song is called "Au clair de la lune."

(89)

Winter Sports

Adapted   NOTE   A. Maillart

In strict time

1. In January weather,
2. A - round the mill - pond glid - ing,

We run out - doors to - geth - er,
In i - cy cir - cle slid - ing,

We take our skates and sleds and go
With skates and sleds we have good fun

Out - side where all is white with snow.
Till sun - set tells us day is done.

Sing and compare these intervals:

(1)   (2)   (3)

Trees in Winter

Adapted   NOTE   Chopin

Smoothly

1. Do the winds of cold De - cem - ber
2. While the win - ter winds are blow - ing,

Help the for - est trees re - mem - ber
Ti - ny leaf buds, slow - ly grow - ing,

How their green and leaf - y dress - es
Lie on all the bar - ren branch - es,

Sum - mer shade and col - or bring?
Wait - ing for the call of spring.

Chopin, the great Polish musician, wrote this melody as part of a composition for the piano.

The Lonely Shepherd

Adapted   NOTE   Basque Melody
                          sung in South America

Smoothly

Far off in the mead-ow, thro' the grass-es deep,

Roams a youth-ful shep-herd, fol-low-ing his sheep;

Out in an-y weath-er, wind and tem-pest blown,

Still the lit-tle shep-herd walks the hills a - lone.

The Basques live in mountain valleys near the Spanish-French border. Many of them have emigrated to new homes in North and South America.

The Winter Visitor

Unknown   ROTE   J. Wolverton

Not too fast

Jack Frost rapped on the win-dow pane

And knocked on the door with his i-ci-cle cane.

"Ex-cuse me!" I said. "The door is shut tight,

I'd rath-er you did not come in to-night."

So he wrote his name all o-ver the glass,

And the ba-by sneezed as she heard him pass.

Lady Moon

NOTE

Translated   Japanese Children's Song

1. Great is the moon in dark-'ning sky,
2. Great is the moon that smiles on me,

She's nev-er old-er as she rides by;
Sun's lit-tle sis-ter she well may be;

Round as a ball she slow-ly grows,
Now like a glass re-flect-ing light,

Then like a slen-der cres-cent shows;
Then as a comb of am-ber bright;

Spring-time, sum-mer, fall, and win-ter,
Spring-time, sum-mer, fall, and win-ter,

On our land she gen-tly — glows.
On the world she shines — each — night.

Bird Dreams

Translated   NOTE   Swedish Folk Song

1. Rest, drow-sy lit-tle bird-ling,
2. Sleep, drow-sy lit-tle bird-ling,

Head un-der drow-sy wing;
Dream of the shad-y trees;

Dream of the bud-ding flow-ers,
Dream of the leaf-y bow-ers,

Wait-ing the call of spring;
Swayed by the sum-mer breeze;

Dream of the bud-ding flow-ers,
Dream of the leaf-y bow-ers,

Wait-ing the call of spring.
Swayed by the sum-mer breeze.

(95)

Tonal Patterns

How many tonal patterns can you sing? How many can you build?

Play this game: A leader asks someone to sing one of the tonal patterns. If the one chosen sings the pattern correctly, it is his turn to be the leader. Or the leader may sing one of the tonal patterns and ask someone to build it. If he builds it correctly, it is his turn to be the leader.

Polar Bear

Anne Matheson ROTE Anne Matheson

Not too fast

1. Far in north-ern po-lar re-gions lives the po-lar bear;
2. In the spring when ice is thin-ner watch the po-lar bear!

He is not like all the oth-ers with his snow-white hair.
See him to the wa-ter slid-ing with a play-ful air!

See him run, run, run, look-ing for his morn-ing meal!
See him kick, kick, kick, push-ing with his legs be-hind!

It will be a fish or a poor, un-hap-py seal.
See him slide, slide, slide! He has swim-ming on his mind.

He is fierce and he is might-y, is the po-lar bear.
All the North is but a play-ground for the po-lar bear.

Day's Farewell

J. W. Beattie   NOTE   Spanish Melody

Slowly

1. Hear the dis - tant ves - per bell
2. Hear the dis - tant ves - per bell

Ring - ing out the day's fare - well,
Peal - ing out the day's fare - well,

"Time to rest," it seems to say,
"Time to sleep," it seems to ring,

"La - bor ends at close of day."
"Eve - nings peace and com - fort bring."

Flow - ers nod their heads in sleep,
Birds have flown to leaf - y nest.

Woods are wrapped in slum - ber deep,
Na - ture's chil - dren all find rest,

Eve - ning shad - ows slow - ly fall,
Sky is red with set - ting sun,

Twi - light deep - ens o - ver all.
Twi - light deep - ens, day is done.

There is a new rhythm pattern in this song. It is the dotted quarter note followed by an eighth note: ♩. ♪

Compare the dotted quarter note and the quarter note: ♩. ♩

When you chant or step the new pattern, you will notice that you hold the dotted quarter note longer. What makes it longer?

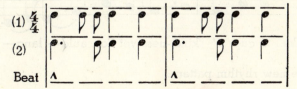

(99)

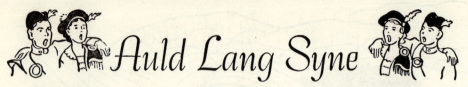

Auld Lang Syne

Robert Burns   ROTE—NOTE   Scottish Tune
Vigorously

1. Should auld ac-quaint-ance be for-got
2. Then here's a hand, my trust-y frien',

And nev-er brought to mind?
And gie's a hand o' thine,

Should auld ac-quaint-ance be for-got
We'll take a cup o' kind-ness yet

And days of auld lang syne?
For auld—— lang—— syne.

For auld— lang— syne, my dear, For auld— lang— syne,

We'll take a cup o' kind-ness yet For auld— lang— syne.

Locate the new rhythm pattern.

(100)

Sailor Chanteys

Chanteys are the work songs sailors used to make up on the old-time sailing vessels. They were usually sung in rhythm with a particular job. A leader and the crew took turns singing in solo and chorus fashion. There are four types of chanteys:

The short-drag chantey was sung for work which required one mighty lift. The crew made that lift as they reached the final word of the chorus.

The halyard chantey was used on work requiring a longer time, such as hoisting sail.

The capstan chantey was sung in marching rhythm as the crew walked around and "wound the capstan." The capstan was a vertical, drumlike cylinder. Around it there was a cable attached to some heavy object on board which had to be moved or to the ship's anchor in the water below. By winding the capstan, the crew could move the heavy object or raise the anchor.

The forecastle chantey was named for the cabin on the forward deck. Here the sailors lived, and in their leisure time they would often sing, dance, and "spin yarns." So the forecastle chantey is likely to have many verses which tell a story. Often the singers made up new verses as they sang.

Rolling King

Traditional   NOTE   Capstan Chantey

In march time

Solo

1. South Aus - tral - ia is my— home.
2. Ain't but— one thing grieves my— mind.
3. Wife, she— stands there on the— quay.

Chorus

Heave a - way!   Heave a - way!

Solo

South Aus - tral - ia is my— home,
Leav - ing— wife and child be - hind,
Shed - ding— tears, she waits for— me,

Sail - ing for Aus - tral - ia.

Chorus

Heave a-way! Heave a - way! Heave a-way, you Roll-ing King!

Heave a -way! Heave a - way! Bound for South Aus - tral - ia!

Blow the Man Down

Traditional   NOTE   Halyard Chantey

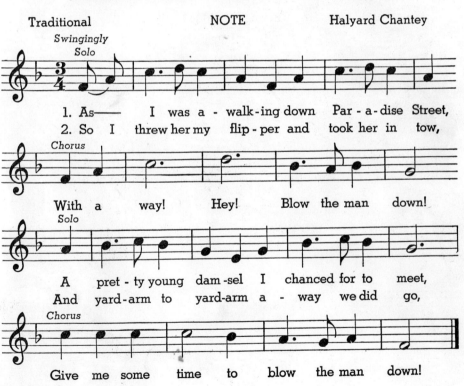

Swingingly
Solo

1. As—— I was a - walk-ing down Par - a - dise Street,
2. So I threw her my flip - per and took her in tow,

Chorus

With a way! Hey! Blow the man down!

Solo

A pret - ty young dam - sel I chanced for to meet,
And yard-arm to yard-arm a - way we did go,

Chorus

Give me some time to blow the man down!

Blow, Ye Winds

Traditional   NOTE   **Forecastle Chantey**

Sturdily
Solo

1. They ad - ver - tise in Bos - ton town,
2. They send you to New Bed - ford fair,
3. They tell you of the clip - per ships,

New York, and Buf - fa - lo,
That fa - mous whal - ing port,
A - go - ing in and out,

Five hun - dred brave A - mer - i - cans
And give you to some stran - gers there
And say, you'll take five hun - dred whale

A - whal - ing for to go.—— Sing - ing
To board and fit you out.—— Sing - ing
Be - fore you're six months out.—— Sing - ing

Chorus

Blow, ye winds of morn - ing! Blow, ye winds, high - o!

Clear a - way your run - ning gear, Blow, ye winds, high - o!

Haul on the Bowlin'

Traditional   ROTE   Short-drag Chantey

Sturdily
Solo

1. Haul on the bow-lin'! The ship, she is a - roll-in'.
2. Haul on the bow-lin'! The bo-sun is a - growl-in'.

Chorus

Haul on the bow-lin', the bow-lin', Haul!——

The Penguin

J. W. Beattie   ROTE   Josephine Kendel

Brightly

1. The pen - guins live 'mid ice and snow
2. With dark - gray back, and front of white,

In the south - ern hem - i - sphere;
Like my dad - dy's eve - ning clothes,

(106)

Just where it is you may not know,
They must pre - sent a fun - ny sight

But it's ver - y far from here;
As they bal - ance on their toes;

As birds, they're not like an - y - thing
Their nests are built on bar - ren stone,

That we have ev - er found,
They dine on smell - y fish,

They can - not fly, tho' they have wings,
To have a pen - guin for our own

But walk and swim a - round.
Is some - thing we all wish.

All Through the Night

Translated   ROTE—NOTE   Welsh Folk Song

Loo——————   Loo——————

1. Sleep, my child, and peace at-tend thee All thro' the night;
2. While the moon her watch is keep-ing All thro' the night;

Loo——————   Loo——————

Guard-ian an-gels God will send thee All   thro' the night.
While the wea-ry world is sleep-ing All   thro' the night,

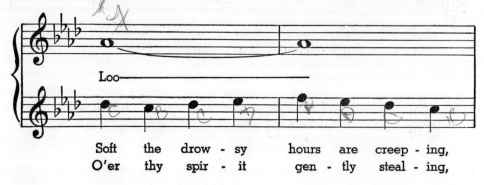

Loo——————

Soft   the   drow - sy   hours   are   creep - ing,
O'er   thy   spir - it   gen - tly   steal - ing,

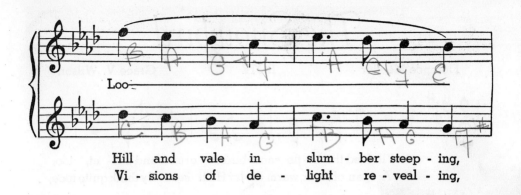

Hill   and   vale   in   slum - ber steep - ing,
Vi - sions   of   de - light   re - veal - ing,

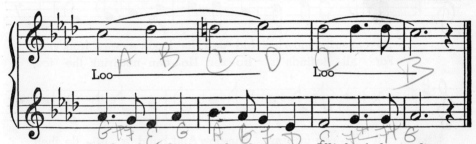

Loo⎯   Loo⎯

Moth-er here her   watch is keep-ing   All thro' the night.
Breathes a pure and   ho - ly feel-ing   All thro' the night.

Who Has Seen the Wind?

1. Who has seen the wind?
   Neither I nor you;
   But when the leaves hang trembling,
   The wind is passing through.

2. Who has seen the wind?
   Neither you nor I;
   But when the trees bow down their heads,
   The wind is passing by.

Chant this poem by Christina Rossetti and then make a tune for it.

(109)

The Snowbird

Florence Meeker   ROTE   Grace V. Wilson

Not too fast

1. I'll feed the lit-tle snow-bird A crumb and su-et, too,
2. A pan of clear, warm wa-ter He'll sure-ly think quite nice,

Be-cause the snow has hid-den His food a-way from view;
For all he finds is fro-zen, He can-not drink the ice;

I'll o-pen up my win-dow And build a lit-tle shelf,
I'm sure he'll thank me kind-ly And stay a-round till spring,

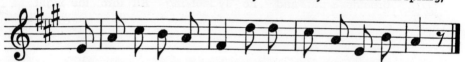

In-vit-ing ev-'ry snow-bird To come and help him-self.
And make us all quite hap-py When we can hear him sing.

Reflections

Adapted   NOTE   Mendelssohn

Slowly, smoothly

A - long the lake dark shad - ows

Re - flect the moun - tain's loft - y steep;

The up - land fields and mead - ows

Lie wrapped in slum - ber deep.

Mendelssohn wrote this melody in his Symphony in A Major, called "The Italian Symphony." Is the melody major or minor? Build the minor key chord.

Brooms

1. On stormy days
   When the wind is high
   Tall trees are brooms
   Sweeping the sky.

2. They swish their branches
   In buckets of rain
   And swash and sweep it
   Blue again.

It will be fun to set this amusing poem to music. It was written by Dorothy Aldis.

(111)

Amalfi Bay

Adapted   ROTE   Italian Folk Song

Brightly

1. A - long the wind-ing streets of old Ra - vel - lo,——
2. The mon - as-ter - y bells are soft - ly ring - ing——

Where foun-tains bright with spar-kling wa - ter play,——
As twi - light ends the long and sun - ny day,——

The laugh-ing chil - dren dance the tar - an - tel - la——
In scent-ed gar - dens night-in-gales are sing - ing——

Far o - ver tran-quil, blue A - mal - fi Bay.——
Far o - ver tran-quil, blue A - mal - fi Bay.——

Night Time

Adapted   NOTE   Italian Folk Song

Moderately

The set - ting sun has turned to red

A - cross the west - ern sky,

And soon, in cloud - banks o - ver - head,

The moon will float on high;

Then ti - ny stars with twin - kling light

A - long the Milk - y Way

Will shine through all the qui - et night

Un - til an - oth - er day.

Moon Balloon

Belle Johnston ROTE Grace V. Wilson

Smoothly

1. To - day I saw a big, round moon
2. And now it has to float and swing

A - way—— in pale blue sky;——
A - bove—— the field and town;——

It looked just like a white bal - loon
The gi - ant child can't reach the string

Some child had tried to fly;——
To hold and pull it down;——

Per - haps a gi - ant child had played,
Of course that's make - be - lieve and play,

Pleased with a toy so grand,——
Real - ly it can't be so,——

And while he skipped and hopped and swayed
But why that moon comes out by day

It flew from out—— his hand.——
I'd sure - ly like—— to know.——

One, Two, Three

Translated   NOTE   Russian Song

In march time

One, two, three! Cou - ra-geous scouts are we,

March-ing brave-ly on-ward we will fight for lib-er - ty!

One, two, three! We sing our joy - ful song,

All the world is bright be-fore us as we march a - long.

This is the song of the Russian Young Pioneers, an organization somewhat like our Boy Scouts and Girl Scouts.

Flag Song

Lydia Ward   ROTE   Jean Hoover

In march time

1. Out on the breeze o'er land and seas,
2. O - ver the brave long may it wave,

A beau - ti - ful ban - ner is stream - ing;
— Peace to the world ev - er bring - ing;

Shin - ing its stars, splen - did its bars
While to the stars, linked with the bars,

Un - der the sun - light are beam - ing.
Hearts will for - ev - er be sing - ing.

Hail to the flag, the beau - ti - ful flag,

The flag that is red, white, and blue!

(116)

Hopak Dancing

Adapted   NOTE   Russian Dance

In strict time

Un - der - neath the can - dle glow,
Cir - cling in a sin - gle row,

To mu - sic of the vi - o - lin,
The ho - pak fig - ures now be - gin.

Leap, stamp, all a-round, Bod-ies near-ly on the ground!

Feet go in and out; Laugh-ing part-ners clap and shout!

The hopak is danced by men and boys who like to display their strength and skill in many ways. They jump into the air and click their heels together, stretch their legs from a squatting position, and leap up and make several turns in the air.

Ground-hog Day

Adapted　　　　　　　　　NOTE　　　　　　　Slavic Dance

Moderately fast

1. Gray old Ground Hog, to - day is Can - dle - mas;
2. Gray old Wood-chuck, the day is bright and cold;

Now, old Ground Hog, con - sult your weath-er glass!
Now, old Wood-chuck, go back in - to your hole!

If the day is fair and light,
When you see your shad - ow clear,

So you see your shad - ow bright,
Warm - er days can - not be near,

Say, old Ground Hog, will win - ter ev - er pass?
Sad old Wood - chuck, long win - ter is fore - told.

Candlemas is the second of February and is better known in this country as Ground-hog Day. The ground hog and the woodchuck are the same animal.

Snow Feathers

Adapted   NOTE   Bohemian Folk Song

In waltz time

1. Snow - flakes   are   float - ing   by,
2. Snow - flakes   are   float - ing   down,

White   feath - ers   fill   the   sky;
White   feath - ers   veil   the   town;

Whirl - ing   and   twirl - ing   go,
Drift - ing   and   sift - ing   there,

Round   and   a - round   they   blow,
Whirl - ing   in   frost - y   air,

White   feath - ers   float - ing   by.
White   feath - ers   float - ing   down.

Sing and build the chord figures in this song.

The Birch Tree

Adapted   NOTE   Russian Folk Song

Not too fast

Bright - est of the   for - est are the   birch   trees,

Straight and tall and   slen - der are the   birch   trees,

Bark   of   sil - ver white - ness   show - ing,

Through   the   lac - y branch - es   glow - ing.

Tschaikowsky, a great Russian composer, used this Russian folk
tune in the Fourth Movement of his Fourth Symphony.

The Parade

Martha Wonn NOTE Martha Wonn

In march time

1. Drum! Drum! Hear the march-ing feet!
2. Drum! Drum! Hear the cym-bals clash!

A par - ade is com - ing down the street.
See the tall drum ma - jor's bat - on flash!

Drum! Drum! Lis - ten to the band!
Drum! Drum! Ban - ners wave on high!

It's the fin - est one in all the land.
Let's sa - lute them now as they pass by.

St. Valentine's Day

Shakespeare   ROTE   English Folk Song

Not too fast

Good mor-row, 'tis— Saint Val-en-tine's Day,

All in— the morn-ing time;—

And I,— a maid— at your win-dow,

To be— your Val-en - tine.—

Your Own Song

While you have been learning music, you have often made up a tune for some favorite verse. If you can create a tune to fit a verse or a verse to fit a tune, why should you not try to make up a complete song, words and music?

Choose some subject that you like, such as a circus parade, an important event, an interesting animal, or a class project on which you are working. Using this subject, make a rhythmical poem, so that you can set it to music. Your poem may rhyme or not, just as you like.

Then, after you have the poem complete, chant it aloud. Does it suggest music to you? If it does, ask your teacher or some musical friend to write the music on the blackboard. When you have the entire song, words and music, just as you like it, copy it into a notebook.

You may find that you can create several songs in this way. And you will be surprised to see how much you can learn about music through creating your own songs.

Paul Revere's Ride

J. W. Beattie   ROTE   J. W. Beattie

Steadily

1. Gal - lop - ing, gal - lop - ing, gal - lop - ing, gal - lop - ing
2. Clat - ter - ing, clat - ter - ing, clat - ter - ing, clat - ter - ing
3. Gal - lop - ing, gal - lop - ing, gal - lop - ing, gal - lop - ing

Through   the   coun - try - side, ——
Down   the   vil - lage   streets, ——
On   the   rid - er   sped, ——

Gal - lop - ing, gal - lop - ing, gal - lop - ing, gal - lop - ing,
Clat - ter - ing, clat - ter - ing, clat - ter - ing, clat - ter - ing,
Gal - lop - ing, gal - lop - ing, gal - lop - ing, gal - lop - ing,

Fast - er, horse - man, ride! ——
Warn - ing all he meets. ——
Men to vic - t'ry led. ——

Old North Church the sig - nal shows,
"On the green at Lex - ing - ton
Men and boys with ball and gun

What it means the rid - er knows.
Gath - er, ev - 'ry moth - er's son!
Stood their ground at Lex - ing - ton,

"Brit - ish troops are draw - ing near,"
Brit - ish troops will soon be here!"
Gath - ered there from far and near,

Cries brave Paul Re - vere.————
Shouts brave Paul Re - vere.————
Called by Paul Re - vere.————

Wise Ben Franklin

Lloyd Norlin   ROTE—NOTE   Lloyd Norlin
Descant

Old   Ben   Frank - lin,

1. Ben - ja - min Frank - lin, in - ven - tive was he;
2. All win - ter long he en - dured bit - ter cold;
3. Friend-ship was need - ed in France in his day;

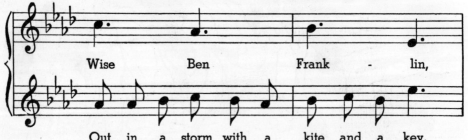

Wise   Ben   Frank - lin,

Out in a storm with a kite and a key,
"There is no way to keep warm," he was told,
Frank - lin was quick - ly sent o - ver that way.

Good   Ben   Frank - lin,

Found how e - lec - tric the   light-ning can be,
Made a fine stove, to this   day it is sold,
Soon there was help for the   young U. S. A.,

Wise   Ben   Frank - lin.

Wise   old   Ben - ja - min   Frank - lin.
Wise   old   Ben - ja - min   Frank - lin.
Wise   old   Ben - ja - min   Frank - lin.

(127)

Washington and Lincoln

Charles Crane   ROTE   Russel Godfrey

Not too fast

1. In February there are days
2. They both be-came our Pres-i-dent

We like to cel-e-brate,
When need for them a-rose,

The birth-days of two fa-mous men
Though not a-like, the great-est men

For ev-er true and great.
Our coun-try ev-er chose.

George Wash-ing-ton is of-ten called
George Wash-ing-ton from ear-ly years

The Fa-ther of our land,
Had wealth and great es-tate,

While   Lin - coln served   in   trou - bled years
But   Lin - coln grew from   pov - er - ty

With   calm and   stead - y   hand.
To   be   a   lead - er   great.

My Flag

Julie Gibault   ROTE   J. Wolverton

Brightly

My flag waves high,   its   stars so   bright

Re - flect the   sil - ver morn - ing   light;

Its thir - teen stripes   and field of   blue

slower

De - light my   heart!   I   will be   true.

Franz Joseph Haydn

(born, 1732; died, 1809)

Franz Joseph Haydn was born in Austria in the year in which George Washington was born in Virginia. Like both Beethoven and Mozart, Haydn showed an interest in music as a small child. He had seen the schoolmaster play a violin; and so, when his parents sang, the boy liked to accompany them on a make-believe violin of two sticks of wood.

Haydn sang in the famous St. Stephen's Cathedral in Vienna during his boyhood. At the same time he learned to play several instruments. He also began composing music while he was a member of the choir school.

When he was a young man, he became conductor of Prince Esterhazy's private orchestra, one of the finest in Europe. Many of his symphonies and string quartets were composed for the musicians under his direction there. His men loved him and called him "Papa Haydn." His cheerful disposition is shown in his music.

Haydn and Mozart were friends, and Beethoven for a time was one of Haydn's pupils.

Haydn's Music

Adapted   ROTE   Haydn

Slowly

1. When Hay-dn was writ-ing his mu-sic in-vit-ing,
2. In Rome and Si-en-na, from Prague to Vi-en-na,
3. Some-time when you're tir-ing of tunes un-in-spir-ing,

The lilt of the light min-u-et was pleas-ant to know.
They danced to the light min-u-et, so grace-ful and slow.
Turn back to the light min-u-et of days long a-go.

This melody is from the slow movement of Haydn's Symphony in G Major.

(131)

The Merry-go-round

Adapted · ROTE · **Haydn**

Brightly

1. The an - i - mals rid - ing the mer - ry - go-round,
2. An or - gan is play - ing, as whirl - ing they go,

An el - e - phant, ze - bra, and kan - ga - roo,
The same lit - tle mel - o - dy all day long;

In jun - gle and cir - cus will nev - er be found;
Sol mi do, sol fa re, sol mi do la sol;

Just rid - ing in cir - cles is all they do.
It sure - ly can't whis - tle a bet - ter song.

Ludwig van Beethoven

(born, 1770; died, 1827)

Ludwig van Beethoven came from a musical family, both his father and his grandfather having been court musicians. Ludwig was given his first music lessons on the harpsichord when he was only four years old. His father was the teacher, and he was a hard taskmaster. The boy had to practice many hours a day and was often dragged out of bed at midnight for lessons. Under such training he mastered the harpsichord, violin, and organ while he was still a child. At the age when boys of today are joining the Boy Scouts, Beethoven was assistant organist in the court chapel and conductor of a theater orchestra.

He enjoyed the out-of-doors and liked to walk through the woods, listening to the sounds which he heard there. Some of the little melodies in his Sixth Symphony, or "Pastoral Symphony," were inspired by his love of nature.

As Beethoven grew older, he became deaf and could no longer hear the music he composed. Still he continued to write music. He produced some of his greatest works under a handicap which would have defeated a less brave man.

Beethoven's Melody

NOTE   Beethoven

Beethoven wrote this melody as the main theme in the final movement of his Ninth Symphony, or "Choral Symphony." Sing the melody or hum it. If it suggests words, sing them.

The Weather Vane

Adapted   ROTE—NOTE   Beethoven

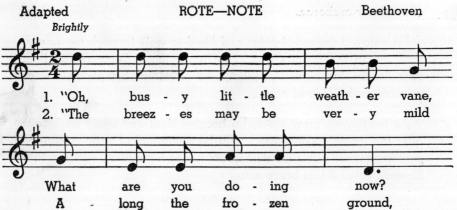

1. "Oh, bus - y lit - tle weath - er vane,
2. "The breez - es may be ver - y mild

What are you do - ing now?
A - long the fro - zen ground,

As mer - ri - ly you turn a - bout,
But here the slight - est puff of air

I al - ways won - der how
Keeps push - ing me a - round;

A - top a slen - der pin - na - cle
Just now I'm driv - en rap - id - ly

So rap - id - ly you spin;
By win - ter's storm - y blast;

No - bod - y down be - low can tell
So now you know the rea - son why

Where head and tail be - gin."
I spin a - bout so fast."

(135)

Hunter and Rabbit

Translated
Brightly

NOTE

German Folk Song

1. Once a hunt - er, seek - ing game,
2. "Do not be a brag - gart bold,
3. Rab - bit hopped and laughed with glee,

Came up - on a rab - bit tame;
I'm a good shot, I've been told;
"What are flow - er tops to me?

Said the man, "What will you do
But your free - dom you may take
I know where some clo - ver grows

If I aim my gun at you?"
If your mis - chief you for - sake;
Sweet - er far than an - y rose;

Rab - bit an - swered, "Mis - ter Man,
Do not chew my flow - ers sweet,
From your gar - den I will stay

Try to shoot me if you can!"
There are oth - er things to eat."
If you put that gun a - way."

Sing and build the tonal patterns.

To Market

Adapted   NOTE   J. J. Wachsmann
(Round)

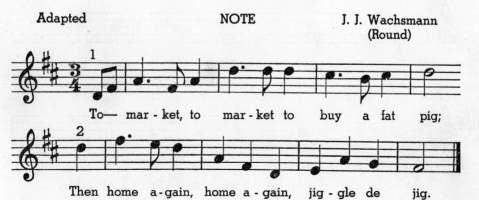

To— mar - ket, to mar - ket to buy a fat pig;

Then home a - gain, home a - gain, jig - gle de jig.

The Little Shepherd

Translated   NOTE   Chilean Singing Game

Moderately

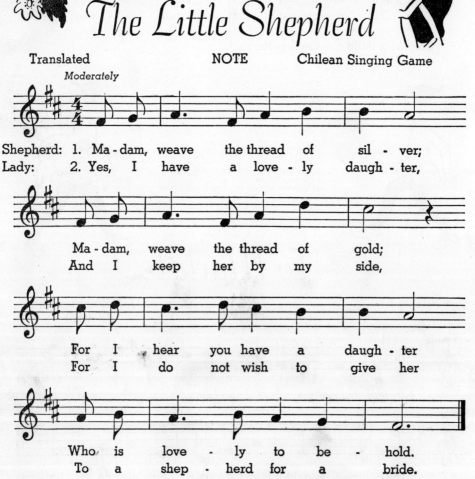

Shepherd: 1. Ma - dam, weave   the thread of   sil - ver;
Lady: 2. Yes, I have   a love - ly   daugh - ter,

Ma - dam, weave   the thread of   gold;
And I keep   her by   my   side,

For I   hear   you have   a   daugh - ter
For I   do   not wish   to   give her

Who is   love - ly   to   be - hold.
To a   shep - herd for   a   bride.

Shepherd: 3. I am going, very angry,
   To the palace of the king,
   And the story of your meanness
   To the royal fam'ly bring.

Lady: 4. Wait a while, my little shepherd,
   Do not be so impolite!
   For the best of all my daughters
   Is the one who comes in sight.

Shepherd: 5. Why, your child is very lovely
   And her face is young and fair,
   I shall never find a better
   Though I wander ev'rywhere.

Lady: 6. And, besides her face and manner,
   She can scrub and sew and cook;
   You will never find a better
   Though a hundred years you look.

Shepherd: 7. Madam, weave the thread of silver;
   Madam, weave the thread of gold;
   I shall wed your little daughter,
   She shall tend my own sheepfold.

Lady: 8. Oh, I thank you, little shepherd,
   And I see you through and through;
   For the child shall be a princess
   Anywhere she goes with you.

In Chile this song is called "El Pastorcito."

Two Friends

Adapted   NOTE   Spanish Melody
sung in New Mexico

Happily

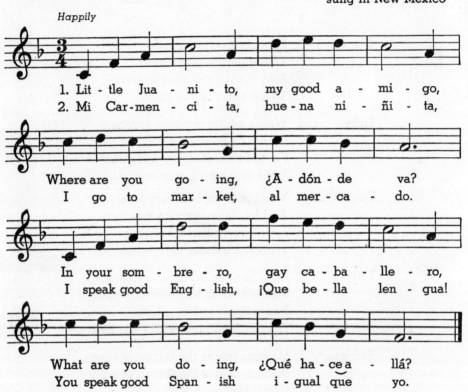

1. Lit - tle Jua - ni - to, my good a - mi - go,
2. Mi Car - men - ci - ta, bue - na ni - ñi - ta,

Where are you go - ing, ¿A - dón - de va?
I go to mar - ket, al mer - ca - do.

In your som - bre - ro, gay ca - ba - lle - ro,
I speak good Eng - lish, ¡Que be - lla len - gua!

What are you do - ing, ¿Qué ha - ce a - llá?
You speak good Span - ish i - gual que yo.

The Spanish words in this song ("Dos Amigos") are pronounced:

Juanito: wahn-ee-toh   Qué hace allá: kay ah-say ahl-yah
Amigo: ah-mee-goh   Carmencita: kar-mane-see-tah
Adónde va: ah-dohn-day vah   Buena niñita: bway-nah neen-yee-tah
Sombrero: sohm-bray-roh   Al mercado: ahl mare-kah-doh
Caballero: kah-bal-yay-roh   Que bella lengua: kay bel-ya len-gwah
Igual que yo: ee-gwahl kay yoh

Put Your Little Foot

Traditional   ROTE   Cowboy Dance

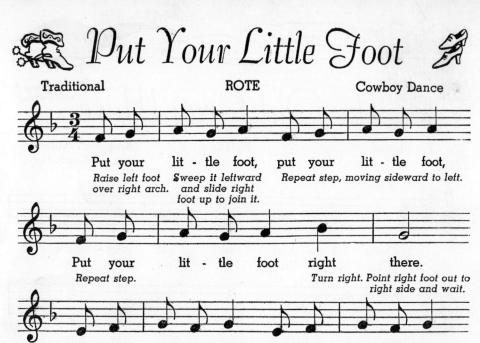

Put your   lit - tle foot,   put your   lit - tle foot,
Raise left foot   Sweep it leftward   Repeat step, moving sideward to left.
over right arch.   and slide right
foot up to join it.

Put   your   lit - tle   foot   right   there.
Repeat step.   *Turn right. Point right foot out to*
right side and wait.

Put your   lit - tle foot,   put your   lit - tle foot,
Raise right foot   Sweep it rightward   Repeat step, moving sideward to right.
over left arch.   and slide left
foot up to join it.

Put   your   lit - tle   foot   right   there.
Repeat step.   *Turn left.*   *Point left foot out to*
left side and wait.

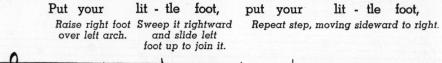

Walk and   walk and walk and   walk and   turn,
Partners walk 4 steps to right.   *Turn right.*

Walk and   walk and walk and   walk and   turn.
Walk 4 steps to left.   *Turn left.*

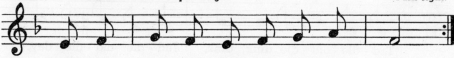

Choose partners and form a single circle, with the boy behind the
girl, arms extended and hands joined. Then follow directions.

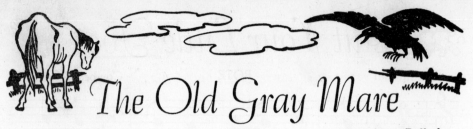

The Old Gray Mare

Traditional ROTE American Ballad
sung in Kentucky

Quite fast

1. Once I had an old gray mare,
2. Old Black Crow was fly - ing by,

Once I had an old gray mare,
Old Black Crow was fly - ing by,

Once I had an old gray mare,
Old Black Crow was fly - ing by,

And her tail was thin and her back was bare.
Says, "Your old gray mare will— sure - ly die."

Chorus

Tad - dle did - dle dink dink, Tad - dle did - dle day,

Tad - dle did - dle dink dink, Tad - dle did - dle day.

3. If she dies I'll tan her skin, etc.,
   If she lives I'll ride her home again.

4. She got so poor I couldn't ride, etc.,
   And her ribs stuck out right through her side.

5. Then I turned her down the creek, etc.,
   To find a little grass to eat.

6. She ate so much while walking there, etc.,
   You would scarcely know the old gray mare.

Lone Star Trail

Traditional   NOTE   American Ballad

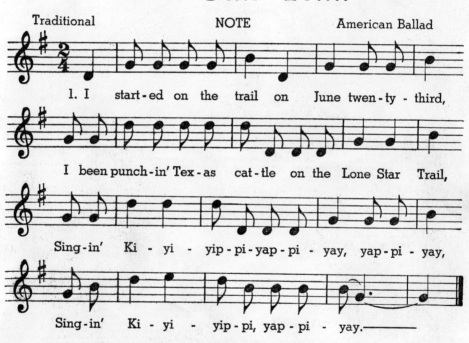

1. I start-ed on the trail on June twen-ty-third,

I been punch-in' Tex-as cat-tle on the Lone Star Trail,

Sing-in' Ki - yi - yip-pi-yap-pi - yay, yap-pi - yay,

Sing-in' Ki - yi - yip-pi, yap-pi - yay.——

2. I'm up in the mornin' before daylight;
   And before I sleep, the moon shines bright, etc.

3. Oh, it's bacon and beans most ev'ry day,
   I'd as soon be eatin' prairie hay, etc.

4. With my knees in the saddle and my seat in the sky,
   I'll quit punchin' cows in the sweet by-and-by, etc.

Good-by, Old Paint

Traditional　　　　　　　　NOTE　　　　　　Cowboy Ballad

1. My—— foot in the stir - rup, my po - ny won't stand,——
2. I'm a - rid - in' Old Paint an' a - lead - in' Old Fran,——

I'm leav - in' Chey - enne an' I'm off for Mon - tan'.——
Good - by, lit - tle An - nie, I'm off for Mon - tan'.——

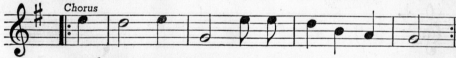

Good - by, Old Paint, I'm a - leav - in' Chey - enne.

3. Oh, keep yourself by me as long as you can,
   Good-by, Little Annie, I'm off for Montan'.

4. Oh, hitch up your hosses and feed 'em some hay,
   And seat yourself by me as long as you stay.

5. My hosses ain't hungry, they'll not eat your hay,
   My wagon is loaded and rollin' away.

(145)

The Bears' Lullaby

Translated   NOTE   Latvian Folk Song

Slowly

1. Ai ja ju ju, Cubs are sleep-ing, Ai ja ju-u-ju,
2. Ai ja ju ju, Fast they're grow-ing, Ai ja ju-u-ju,
3. Ai ja ju ju, Now they're wak-ing, Ai ja ju-u-ju,

A - pril skies are soft - ly weep-ing, Ju ju ju.
For-est trees new green are show - ing, Ju ju ju.
Hon-ey sweet they'll soon be tak - ing, Ju ju ju.

Pronounce the opening syllables as follows: Ai, I; ja, ya; ju, you.

Yellow Hair

Translated   NOTE   Ute (Indian) Song

Yel - low Bear with tou - sled hair,

Come out - side and feel the air,

Win - ter's gone a - way, Spring is here to stay.

(146)

Sing to God

Adapted NOTE Joseph Pleyl

In march time

1. Chant thanks - giv - ing, march a - long,
2. Sing to God, the Heav'n - ly King,

Lift - ing hearts on wings of song!
Let our voic - es proud - ly ring!

Giv - ing thanks for hap - py days,
Sing our great Cre - a - tor's praise,

Sing we our Cre - a - tor's praise.
Glo - rious all His works and ways.

Little Ole

Translated   ROTE   O. Jacobsen

Gently

1. When lit - tle   O - le with his um - brel - la
2. To all the   sleep - ers who in   the   day - time
3. He tells of   moon - beams that shine   so   bright - ly

Comes in the   night - time, the fun - ny   fel - low,
Have been good   chil - dren in work and   play - time,
A - mid the   star - lets that twin - kle   night - ly,

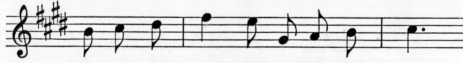

O'er drow - sy   chil - dren he nods his   head,
He whis - pers   sto - ries of long   a -   go,
And ho - ly   an - gels who watch   a -   bove,

Then gen - tly   leaves them a - sleep in   bed.
Which on - ly   O - le can sure - ly   know.
O'er sleep - ing   chil - dren they guard and   love.

Siembamba

Translated   NOTE   South African Folk Song

Moderately

1. Siem-bam-ba, I'm a ba - by, Siem-bam-ba, I'm a ba - by,
2. Siem-bam-ba, See me grow-ing, Siem-bam-ba, See me grow-ing,

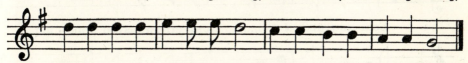

Safe-ly here I lie on your lap, Smil-ing thro' my morn-ing nap.
Soon I'll be a tall, stur-dy lad, Some-times good and some-times bad.

3. Siembamba, When I'm older,
   Siembamba, When I'm older,
   From her lap I'll leap to the ground,
   Hunt the game for miles around.

4. Siembamba, I shall marry,
   Siembamba, I shall marry,
   Though my mother thinks I'm her own,
   Won't believe that I am grown.

5. Siembamba, All are babies,
   Siembamba, All are babies;
   Even old men, bent and gray,
   Still are children, so they say.

Siembamba means rockaby or lullaby.

(149)

Northern Swans

Translated
Smoothly

NOTE

Icelandic Folk Song

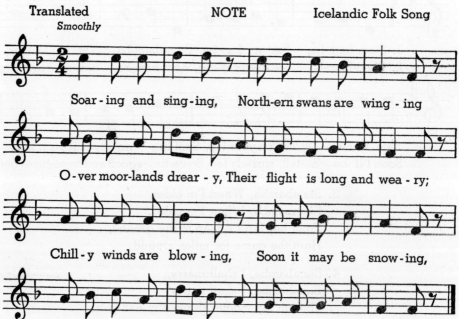

Soar - ing and sing - ing,   North-ern swans are wing - ing

O - ver moor-lands drear - y, Their flight is long and wea - ry;

Chill - y winds are blow - ing,   Soon it may be snow - ing,

Chil-dren leave their play - ing To search for lamb-kins stray - ing.

Iceland is an island lying in the North Atlantic. It is about the size of the state of Kentucky. Iceland is famous for its ancient legends known as sagas. Many of the folk songs are about elves and the great northern swans.

Moonlight

Translated   NOTE   Icelandic Folk Song

Brightly

1. Dream-ing in the moon-light, I lin-gered near a wood.
2. Spur-ring snow-y charg-ers, they rode a - long the ground,
3. Laugh-ing as she hailed me, the queen of night went by,

Lit - tle elves came rid - ing a - bout me where I stood;
Charg-ers' hoofs a - twin-kle tho' mak-ing not a sound,
Rid - ing to her pal - ace be - neath the moun-tain high;

Sound - ing gold - en bu - gles, they burst up - on my sight,
Bright as north-ern swans fly - ing o'er the heath-er brown,
Does she know the se - cret that trou - bles me of late,

Chim - ing their bells in the clear, star - ry night,
White feath-ers shin - ing and songs float - ing down,
Sound - ing a warn - ing that tells of my fate,

Chim - ing their bells in the clear, star - ry night.
White feath-ers shin - ing and songs float - ing down.
Sound - ing a warn - ing that tells of my fate?

(151)

My Kite

Ina W. Hall   ROTE   H. Hinga

Gaily

1. Lit - tle kite, so high in A - pril sky,
2. Lit - tle kite, so high in A - pril sky,

Please tell me from a - far,————
Are you a small bal - loon?————

Will you show at night a bea - con light
Will you break the string and then take wing

And twin - kle like a star?————
To sail on toward the moon?————

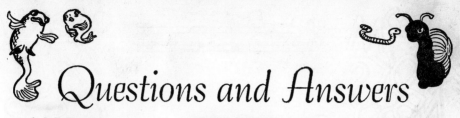

Questions and Answers

J. W. Beattie
Gaily

ROTE—NOTE

Old Tune

Little Fish: 1. "May I go out for a swim in the air?"
Baby Owl: 2. "May I go out for a trip in the park?"

Mother: "Oh, yes, you may go, lit - tle daugh-ter,————
Father: "Why, cer - tain - ly, this ver - y eve-ning,————

But keep your fins wet and be sure to take care
But stay in the nest till a - long aft - er dark,

Not to stay too long out of the wa - ter."————
For the night is the best time for see - ing."————

Baby Turtle: 3. "May I go challenge the rabbit to race?"
Father: "Why, surely, you'd better start creeping;
By steadily going at Grandfather's pace,
You can win while the rabbit is sleeping."

Worm: 4. "Why do you carry that shell on your back?"
Snail: "I'll answer you very demurely:
You see, if I'm out in a robin's attack,
I can stay in my shell-hole securely."

The Alphabet

Irma Davis   NOTE   Jamie Sisson

1. C B S and N B C
2. If I live on R F D,

Bring ex - cit - ing news to me;
Then I can R S V P

S O S and T N T
When a par - cel comes for me

Al - ways, al - ways fright - en me.
Bear - ing let - ters C O D.

3. Mother goes to PTA;
   IOU means "I must pay."
   When I am too ill to play,
   MD comes till I'm OK.

4. Six A.M. comes all too soon;
   P.M. means the afternoon;
   Sure I am that you will see
   U.S.A. mean most to me.

Sing and build the chord figures.

Frog and Owl

B. Peters   NOTE   B. Peters

1. Once an old green frog from his nice cool bog
2. Then the owl on high from his tree near by

Saw an owl in a tree near by.
Hoot - ed low from a hick - 'ry limb,

"Can you hop," croaked he, "from the ground to the tree?"
"Can you fly, old frog, from your nice chill - y bog?"

Said the owl, "Why, no, I fly!"
Said the frog, "Why, no, I swim!"

Is this song major or minor?

The Streamliner

Ruth Wilson Kelsey NOTE Grace V. Wilson

Fast

1. "Can you catch me, can you catch me?"
2. Mad - ly dash - ing, loud - ly clash - ing,

Says the stream - line train,
O - ver hill and plain,

Head - light shin - ing, si - ren whin - ing,
"Can you catch me, can you catch me?"

Rac - ing like a plane.
Says the stream - line train.

Spring Awakes

Adapted · ROTE · German Folk Song

Smoothly

Brooks have burst their i - cy crust,

Win - ter snow is go - ing;

A - pril wind be - comes a breeze,

Gen - tle is its blow - ing;

Tril - liums in the wood - land peep,

Win - ter's gone and spring a - wakes from sleep.

The Thief

Translated NOTE German Folk Song

Steadily

1. Fox, you stole our goose, you rob - ber,
2. Mis - ter Fox, if you are clev - er,

Bring her back a - gain! Bring her back a - gain!
You will bring her back! You will bring her back!

If you don't, the hun - ter'll track you,
We had planned to serve her Sun - day,

Shoot you with his shin - ing gun,
When the fam - - 'ly's at our house,

He will track you down and shoot you with his shin - ing gun.
We will have that goose on Sun - day; you can eat a mouse!

Sing and build the tonal patterns.

Sunrise

Adapted   ROTE   Liszt

Slowly

1. The last pale stars are fad - ing
2. The east - ern skies are glow - ing

Through clouds of mist - y gray,——
With hues of ros - y light,——

While drow - sy earth,—— still sleep - ing,
When o'er the far—— hor - i - zon

A - waits the dawn—— of day.——
The sun breaks in - to sight.——

Franz Liszt was a great Hungarian composer. He and Johannes Brahms lived at the same time.

(159)

Old Fisherman

Chi Tung Tsu   ROTE   Chinese River Song

Slowly

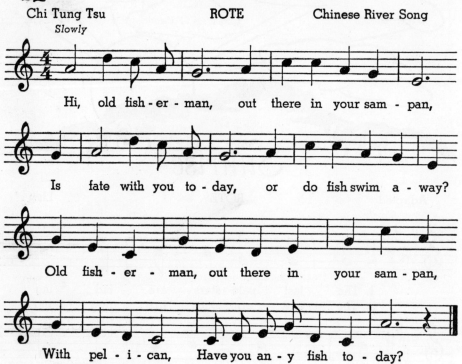

Hi, old fish - er - man, out there in your sam - pan,

Is fate with you to - day, or do fish swim a - way?

Old fish - er - man, out there in your sam - pan,

With pel - i - can, Have you an - y fish to - day?

Chinese music is often based on a five-tone scale. Fa and ti of our scale are left out. You can play the five-tone scale on the piano by striking only the black keys.

Chinese Girls

Edna Becker · ROTE · Based on a Chinese scale

Not too fast

Lit - tle Chi-nese girls, they say, like to run and skip and play,

Like to learn to sew and cook, read out of a sto - ry book,

Help their moth-ers dust and sweep, rock their ba - by dolls to sleep;

Some-times they are naugh-ty, too, do the things they should-n't do.

Lit - tle Chi-nese girls must be ver - y, ver - y much like me.

The Sandman

Translated
Quietly

ROTE

Brahms

1. There's mag-ic in the moon-beam that kissed the flow'rs good night,
2.   I see a friend-ly elf man, he holds a bag of sand,

For now the red, red rose-buds are pale as lil-ies white;
He bought it from the elf folk in their en-chant-ed land;

The pine trees still are whis-p'ring, the crick-et rings his bell,
Up-on your drow-sy eye-lids some gold-en grains he'll strew,

All for you, all for you, to make you slum-ber well.
That, you know, that, you know, will make your dream come true.

A Gypsy Song

Adapted   NOTE   Hungarian Dance

Fast

Gyp-sies, mak-ing camp on field and heath-er,
Mov-ing in a ring, their bod-ies sway-ing,

Gath-er near the blaz-ing fire to-geth-er;
Dance to vi-o-lin and zith-er play-ing.

Slower   *Fast*

Part-ners read-y, quick-ly all ad-vanc-ing,
Move-ment slow-er, arm and bod-y bend-ing,

Slower   *Fast*

For-ward stead-y, in a cir-cle danc-ing;
Bow-ing low-er, now the step is end-ing.

Brahms enjoyed watching gypsies dance. He used this tune in his Hungarian Dance No. 5.

Welcome to Spring

Adapted   ROTE   French Folk Song

Joyfully

1. New grass from the ground is spring - ing
2. The branch - es of elm and ma - ple

As winds from the south - land blow;
Are dressed in their soft - est green;

Full brooks to the lake are bring - ing
Bright blos - soms in wood and mead - ow

Their wa - ters of melt - ed snow.
Add joy to the wood - land scene.

Blue is the sky, A - pril winds sigh, All

Na - ture a - wak - ens from a slum - ber deep, Win - ter, good - by!

In Switzerland

Translated ROTE Swiss Folk Song

Not too fast

1. My fa - ther is from Ap - pen - zell,
2. My moth - er's Swiss, oh, yes, in - deed,
3. My fa - ther loves to sing and dance,

Yoo ree ree, yoo ree ree!

He eats his cheese, the plate as well,
Has lace to make and goats to feed,
On week - days wears his Sun - day pants,

Yoo ree ree, yo ho!

Yoo ree ree, yoo ree ree, Yoo ree ree ree ree, yo ho!

Yoo ree ree, yoo ree ree, Yoo ree ree, yo ho!

K. Whitmore   NOTE   F. X. Suessmayer

Not too fast

1. Fair A-pril, the maid-en, comes down from the sky,
2. She flings her bright jew-els on pas-ture and lawn,

Her tress-es are gold-en, and blue is her eye;
To spar-kle and shine in the light of the dawn;

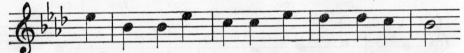

Her glance is re-flect-ed in stream and in lake,
She warms the green moss where the wind-flow-ers lie,

At sound of her voice all the flow-ers a-wake.
And teach-es the blue-bird a tune of the sky.

Hiking Song

Translated   ROTE   Swiss Hiking Song

Steadily

I have brok-en do on my clar-i-net, oh,

I have bro-ken do— on my clar - i - net;

What will pa-pa say to me, tra la la?

What will ma-ma say to me, tra la la?

In step, com - a - rades; in step, com - a - rades; In

step, tra la la la; In step, com - a - rades; in

step, com - a - rades; In step, tra la la la!

Repeat the song, singing, "I have broken re," etc. Then repeat again, singing, "I have broken mi," and so on until you have used the entire scale.

The Band

Adapted NOTE French Folk Song

1. Come, let's run and hur - ry to the square;
2. Go quite near as peo - ple gath - er round,

Oh, what fun! A band is play - ing there.
You will hear a loud and stir - ring sound!

Clar - i - net and o - boe, dee - dle dee - dle do do,
Pic - co - lo and bass drum, dee - dle dee - dle dum dum,

Flute and slide trom - bone and mel - low bar - i - tone.
Horn and deep bas - soon, they play a jol - ly tune.

sol fa sol sol fi sol
do ti do

Dandelions

Edna Becker   ROTE—NOTE   Grace V. Wilson

1. The lit - tle stars came down last night
2. They left their spar - kling foot - prints there,

And played up - on my lawn;
You'll see them as you pass:

When morn - ing came and I looked out,
My lawn is filled with dan - de - lions,

The stars them - selves were gone.
All shin - ing in the grass.

Compare the two tonal patterns. When a sharp is placed before a note, it raises the tone a half step. When fa is sharped, we call it fi. We call this kind of tone a sharp chromatic. The second tonal pattern sounds like do ti do.

Our Garden

Translated NOTE French Singing Game

1-3. Come, see how to make a gar-den grow,

Peas, beans, let-tuce, cab-bage, row by row.
Corn, beet, rad-ish, car-rot, row by row.
Chard, to - ma-to, spin-ach, row by row.

First we dig and cul - ti - vate the soil,
Na - ture's help-ers — wa - ter, sun, and toil—
Cut and clean, with vin - e - gar and oil,

And then we cov - er all the seeds we sow.
Will start the seed-lings from the ground be - low.
They make a sal - ad ev - 'ry - one should know.

The Organ Grinder

Adapted · ROTE—NOTE · Tschaikowsky

sol fi sol

In waltz time

1. Here comes the or - gan grind - er,
2. See how he keeps on grind - ing,

Mel - o - dy loud - ly sound - ing,
Chil - dren all gath - er round him,

Al - ways a glad re - mind - er,
Sum - mer - time pleas - ure find - ing,

Sum-mer is fol-low-ing soon.——
Danc-ing and sing-ing a tune.——

The new sign in the tonal pattern is called a natural. When a natural is placed before a note which is flatted in the signature, it cancels the flat and therefore raises the tone a half step. A tone with a flat canceled is treated like a sharped tone and given a sharp chromatic name.

(172)

Slovak Dance

Adapted   NOTE   Slovak Dance

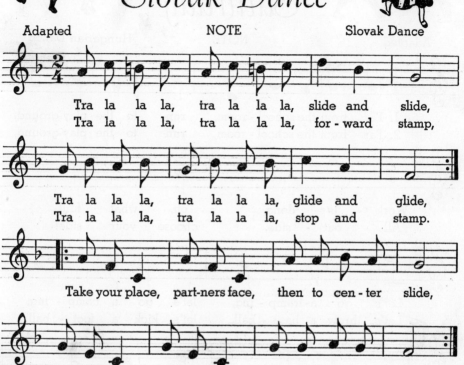

Tra la la la,   tra la la la,   slide and   slide,
Tra la la la,   tra la la la,   for - ward   stamp,

Tra la la la,   tra la la la,   glide and   glide,
Tra la la la,   tra la la la,   stop and   stamp.

Take your place,   part-ners face,   then to cen - ter   slide,

Still in place,   part-ners face,   back-ward now we   glide.

Choose partners and form a single circle, with the girl to the right of the boy. Join hands in the circle.

Staff 1: 8 slides to left. Stamp on the last note.

Staff 2: 8 slides to right and stamp.

Staff 1: 3 steps to center and stamp; 3 steps back to place and stamp.

Staff 2: Partners hook right elbows and circle in place with 4 step-hops. Stamp.

Staff 3: Partners face and take 4 slow slides to center.

Staff 4: Return to place with 4 slow slides.

Staff 3: 2 slides to center and 2 back to place.

Staff 4: Hook right elbows and circle 4 step-hops

(173)

mi ri mi

Saturday

Adapted   NOTE   Hungarian Dance

1. Far from the school-room, run to the play-ground,
2. Far from the school-room, run to the play-ground,

Work is done, oh, what fun!
All out-side, choose your side!

Let's go a-tramp-ing, let's go a-camp-ing,
Let's throw a base-ball, let's kick a foot-ball,

Sat-ur-day, time for play!
Sat-ur-day, time for play!

Spring

Adapted   NOTE   Netherlands Folk Song
(Canon)

1. There's mu-sic in the branch-es high,
2. There's col-or on the ground be-low,

The thrash - er sings in woods near by;
The but - ter - cups in pas - tures grow;

Spring flow'rs in mead - ows now are seen,
The ap - ple trees are blos - som - ing

All the elms are dressed in green.
In the mer - ry time of spring.

May Bells

Adapted   NOTE   English Canon

1. White cor - al bells up - on a slen - der stalk,
2. Oh, don't you wish that you might hear them ring?

Lil - ies of the val - ley deck my gar - den walk.
That can hap - pen on - ly when the elves all sing.

A canon is much like a round and is sung in the same manner.

Roller Skating

Adapted NOTE Hungarian Dance

Fast

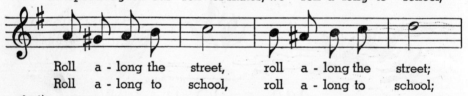

1. Speed-ing on our roll - er skates, we roll a - long the street;
2. Speed-ing on our roll - er skates, we roll a - long to school;

Roll a - long the street, roll a - long the street;
Roll a - long to school, roll a - long to school;

Watch-ing out for mo-tor cars and peo-ple we may meet;
Watch-ing out for mo-tor cars, o - bey-ing traf-fic rules;

Speed-ing on our roll - er skates, we roll on the street.
Speed-ing on our roll - er skates, we roll on to school.

Sing these tonal patterns:

The Mist

Nellie B. Miller

NOTE

J. Wolverton

Mysteriously

1. The mist is a soft, white puss - y cat
2. And then — the sun - shine runs a - way

That creeps so shy and still———
To hide be - yond the hill,———

— Up from the wil - lows by the brook
For fear of this soft, white, creep - ing cat

And crouch - es on the hill.———
The whole wide world is still.———

Street Calls

J. W. Beattie

NOTE

Old Tune with calls
from Ohio and Kansas

In waltz time

1. Quite late in the spring when the fur-nace is out,
2. In A-pril and May when the weath-er is right,
3. In sum-mer when or-chards and gar-dens are green,
4. Now, man-y there are who call out in the street

A rag-ged old man comes a-long;———
The fish sell-er starts on his rounds;———
The truck-gar-den man comes our way;———
A jin-gle in tune and in rhyme;———

We run out to greet him with laugh-ter and shout,
His cu-ri-ous call is our great-est de-light,
The queer-est old fel-low you ev-er have seen,
Just care-ful-ly lis-ten, so you can re-peat

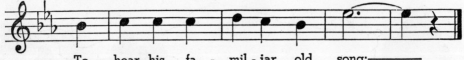

To hear his fa-mil-iar old song:———
And this is the way that it sounds:———
His mar-ket-ing song seems to say:———
Their calls when we're sing-ing next time.———

Calls

ROTE
1. THE CHIMNEY SWEEP

Sweep'em up, sweep'em down, Hi - le - ho! Hi - le - ho!

2. THE FISH SELLER

Fish to-day! Fish to-day! White-fish! Her-ring!

Cat-fish! Perch! Fresh to-day! Fresh to-day!

3. THE VEGETABLE MAN

Po - ta - toes! To - ma - toes! Ap-ples! Peach-es!

Cab-bage! Sweet corn! Come and see! Here I be!

The Humming Bird

Evelyn Corey   ROTE   David Geppert

Not too fast

A hum-ming bird sang to a gold-en flow'r,

"Oh, may I bring you an A—— pril show'r?"

Then he sang to a crim-son rose,

"Will you nod your head if a gen-tle wind blows?

Will you nod your head if a gen-tle wind blows?"

A pass-ing stran-ger heard him say,

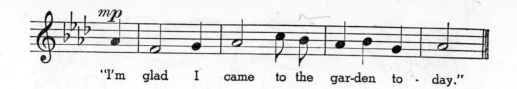

"I'm glad I came to the gar-den to - day."

Bird and Flower

Ruth Wilson Kelsey   **ROTE**   Jamie Sisson

Swingingly

1. O-ri-ole, there in the tree-top, trill-ing a song of spring,—
2. Daf-fo-dil, bright in the gar-den, what did the breez-es say,—

I can tell you're hap-py, too, joy - ful - ly you sing.—
When they came to play with you? Dark - 'ning was the day.—

What is the name of your so - lo, please won't you tell me now?—
Can you not whis-per the se - cret? What did they say to you?—

Some fine day I'll sing—with you, if— you teach me how.—
Spring-time flow'rs will nev - er tell, still— I wish I knew.—

What Can the Matter Be?

Traditional   ROTE   English Folk Song

In swinging rhythm

Oh, dear! What can the mat-ter be?

Dear, dear! What can the mat-ter be?

Oh, dear! What can the mat-ter be?

End

John-ny's so long at the fair.————

1. He prom-ised to buy me a bunch of blue rib-bons,
2. He prom-ised he'd bring me a bas-ket of po-sies,

He prom-ised to buy me a bunch of blue rib-bons,
A gar-land of lil-ies, a gar-land of ros-es,

(182)

He prom-ised to buy me a bunch of blue rib-bons
A lit-tle straw hat to set off the blue rib-bons

Go to the beginning

To tie up my bon - ny brown hair.——— And it's
That tie up my bon - ny brown hair.——— And it's

Nobody Knows

Helen Coale Crew   ROTE   J. Wolverton

Smoothly

1. Winds of the morn - ing, bend - ing the grass - es,
2. Winds of the eve - ning, dance in the tree - tops,

Drink - ing the dew - drops, kiss - ing the rose,
Sweep a - way clouds from the moon till she glows;

Where are you go - ing when mead - ows are qui - et
Why don't you blow far a - way the old Sand-man

slower

And sleep - y at noon-time? No - bod - y knows.
That makes me so sleep - y? No - bod - y knows.

(183)

The Rainbow

J. W. Beattie ROTE Irish Melody (adapted)

1. Aft - er a show - er, one fine A - pril day,
2. Aft - er a show - er, a beau - ti - ful sight

I chanced to look up and be - fore me there lay
To glad - den the world with its ra - di - ant light,

An arc of pure col - ors a - cross the pale sky,
The band of bright col - ors in glo - ri - ous blend

A glow thro' the clouds swift - ly pass - ing by.
Is rich - er than gold at the rain - bow's end.

mi ri mi re di re

How Creatures Move

Unknown　　　　　ROTE—NOTE　　　　　Eleanor Vaught

Not too fast

The li-on walks on pad-ded paws,
The worm can wig-gle all a-round,

The squir-rel leaps from limb to limb,
The mon-key dan-gles by his tail,

While flies can crawl straight on the wall,
The birds can hop up-on the ground,

And seals can dive and swim.
Or spread their wings and sail.

slower
But boys and girls have much more fun,

faster
They leap and dance and walk and run.

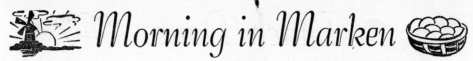

Morning in Marken

Adapted   NOTE   Netherlands Folk Song

In waltz time

1. Bright-ly the sun shines o-ver the Zui-der Zee,
2. Peo-ple are here from E-dam and Vol-len-dam,

Pull on your clothes as fast as can be;
Mar-ket piled high with chees-es and ham;

Wood-en shoes clat-ter-ing, bus-y tongues chat-ter-ing,
Wood-en shoes clat-ter-ing, bus-y tongues chat-ter-ing,

Warn of the crowd we soon are to see.
Sound all the way to Mon-nick-en - dam.

Marken is a small island in the Zuider Zee. To its weekly market come people from the near-by towns to buy and sell things. Visitors also come to see the quaint costumes of Old Holland which the people wear to market.

(187)

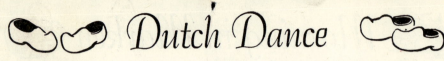

Dutch Dance

Adapted   NOTE   Netherlands Singing Game

In waltz time

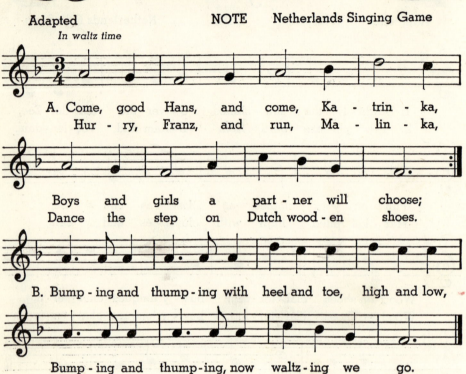

A. Come, good Hans, and come, Ka - trin - ka,
Hur - ry, Franz, and run, Ma - lin - ka,

Boys and girls a part - ner will choose;
Dance the step on Dutch wood - en shoes.

B. Bump - ing and thump - ing with heel and toe, high and low,

Bump - ing and thump - ing, now waltz - ing we go.

Partners face each other, with hands on hips. (A) The boy steps on his left foot while the girl steps on her right foot. The other foot is swung across in front with a brushing movement, lifting the body up for a hop on the supporting foot. This step-brush-hop continues to the count of one, two, three, alternating from side to side. (B) Partners join hands, outstretched to the side, and turn with a hopping waltz step.

Susie, Little Susie

Paraphrased   NOTE   German Folk Song

1. Su - sie, lit - tle Su - sie, now what is the news?
2. Su - sie, lit - tle Su - sie, a pen - ny now, please!

The geese are go - ing bare - foot be - cause they've no shoes;
To buy a lit - tle sup - per of rye bread and cheese;

The cob - bler has leath - er, he'll make them a pair,
I'll sell my fine mat - tress and stay wide a - wake,

All the lit - tle gos - lings will have shoes to wear.
Buy a lit - tle sup - per of ice cream and cake.

Humperdinck introduced this old song into his opera "Hänsel and
Gretel."

(189)

Swinging

Florence Meeker ROTE **Grace V. Wilson**
Descant by Ewald Nolte

1. My swing, hung from branch - es
2. Just see, float - ing sky - ward

1. My swing is hung from branch - es
2. Just see me float - ing sky - ward

Up high in ma - ple tree.
Al - most to shak - ing leaves.

Up high in the ma - ple tree.
Al - most to the shak - ing leaves.

The rope is tied se - cure - ly
Pre - tend I'm par - a - chut - ing,

The rope is tied se - cure - ly
Pre - tend I'm par - a - chut - ing,

And strong e-nough for me.——
As breez-es tug my sleeves.——

And strong e-nough—— for me.——
As breez-es tug—— my sleeves.

To the Woods

NOTE

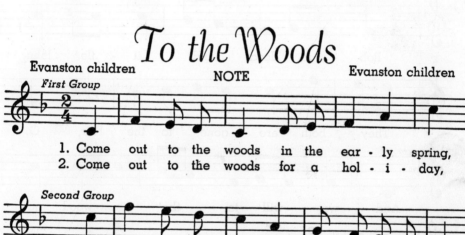

Evanston children   Evanston children

First Group

1. Come out to the woods in the ear-ly spring,
2. Come out to the woods for a hol-i-day,

Second Group

The blue-bird and war-bler flash up-on the wing,
The brook rip-ples gai-ly, sing-ing on its way,

First Group

Come out to the woods and the hill-sides green,
Come out to the woods where the wild-flow'rs grow,

Both Groups

Where wild cher-ry bloom and dog-wood are seen.
Come out where the fra-grant spring breez-es blow.

(191)

May Day Carol

Traditional   NOTE   English Carol

Gaily

Rob - in Hood and Lit - tle John,

They both are gone to the Fair, O,

And we will to the green - wood go

To see what they do there, O,

And for to chase the buck and doe,

To chase the buck and doe, O,

And for to chase the buck and doe,

With Hal - an to sing mer - ry, O!

Spring Birds

ROTE—NOTE

Adapted

Gaily

German Folk Song

1. Wing - ing, wing - ing o'er the or - chard lane,
2. Swing - ing, swing - ing from the ma - ple trees,
3. Sing - ing, sing - ing as they flit a - long,

Thrash - er, jay, and mock - ing bird
O - ri - ole and vir - e - o
Hear the bus - y, brown che - wink,

From the branch - es may be heard,
Rock in ham - mocks to and fro,
Mead - ow lark and bob - o - link,

Wing - ing, wing - ing thro' the woods a - gain.
Swing - ing, swing - ing on the pass - ing breeze.
Sing - ing, sing - ing, each his hap - py song.

(193)

Old Woman and the Peddler

Traditional   ROTE   English Folk Song

Not too fast

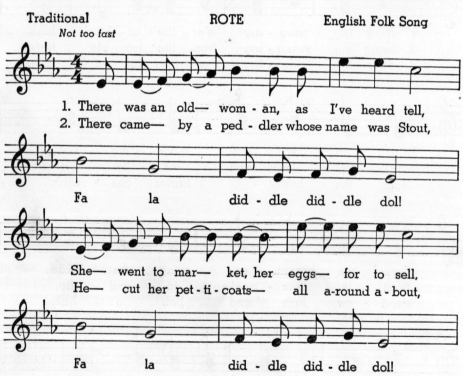

1. There was an old— wom - an, as I've heard tell,
2. There came— by a ped - dler whose name was Stout,

Fa   la   did - dle did - dle dol!

She— went to mar— ket, her eggs— for to sell,
He— cut her pet - ti - coats— all a-round a - bout,

Fa   la   did - dle did - dle dol!

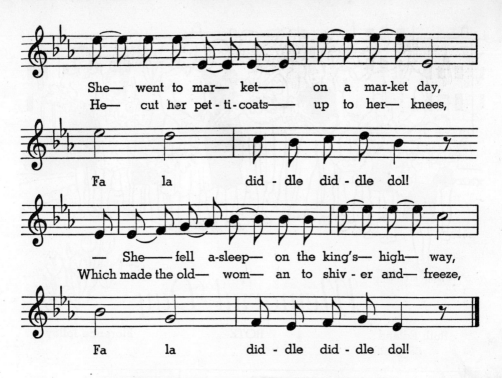

She— went to mar— ket—— on a mar-ket day,
He— cut her pet - ti-coats—— up to her— knees,

Fa la did - dle did - dle dol!

— She—— fell a-sleep— on the king's— high— way,
Which made the old— wom— an to shiv - er and— freeze,

Fa la did - dle did - dle dol!

3. When this little woman did first awake,
   She began to shiver and she began to shake;
   She began to wonder and she began to cry,
   "Lauk-a mercy on me, this is none of I!"

4. "But if it be I, as I hope it be,
   I've a little dog at home and he'll know me;
   If it be I, he'll wag his little tail;
   And if it be not I, he'll only bark and wail."

5. Home went the old woman, all in the dark;
   Up got the little dog and he began to bark,
   He began to bark and she began to cry,
   "Lauk-a mercy on me, this is none of I!"

Memorial Day

Ruth Edland
Reverently

ROTE

Florence Jolley

What can I do on Me - mo - rial Day

To hon - or our fall - en men?

What can I do on Me - mo - rial—— Day

To show I re - mem - ber then?

I can bring a rose of fier - y red,

A lil - y of pur - est white,

An i - ris, too, of clear - est blue;

The three will— be just right.

I will proud - ly hail our glo - rious flag

For which men fought and bled;

And then right there I'll breathe a prayer:

God bless our he - ro - ic dead!

The Star-Spangled Banner

Francis Scott Key ROTE John Stafford Smith

Moderately

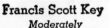

1. Oh,—— say, can you see,—— by the dawn's ear - ly
2. On the shore, dim - ly seen— thro' the mists of the
3. Oh,—— thus be it ev - er when— free - men shall

light, What so proud - ly we hailed at the twi-light's last
deep, Where the foe's haugh-ty host in dread si - lence re -
stand Be - tween their lov'd homes and the war's des - o -

gleam - ing, Whose broad stripes and bright stars, thro' the
pos - es, What is that which the breeze, o'er the
la - tion! Blest with vic - t'ry and peace, may the

per - il - ous fight, O'er the ram - parts we watched were so
tow - er - ing steep, As it fit - ful - ly blows, half con -
Heav'n-res-cued land Praise the Pow'r that hath made and pre-

gal - lant - ly stream-ing? And the rock - et's red glare, the bombs
ceals, half dis - clos - es? Now it catch-es the gleam of the
served us a na - tion! Then— con-quer we must, when our

burst-ing in air, Gave— proof thro' the night— that our
morn-ing's first beam, In full glo - ry re - flect-ed now—
cause it is just, And— this be our mot-to: "In—

ff

flag was still there. Oh,— say, does that
shines on the stream. 'Tis the Star - Span - gled
God is our Trust." And the Star - Span - gled

Star - Span - gled Ban - ner yet wave—— O'er the
Ban - ner, Oh, long may it wave—— O'er the
Ban - ner in tri - umph shall wave—— O'er the

land—— of the free and the home of the brave?
land—— of the free and the home of the brave!
land—— of the free and the home of the brave.

Tonal Patterns

How many tonal patterns can you sing? Make up some games to play with these tonal patterns.

Classified Index

(203)

Index of Songs

(204)

PAGE	TITLE	AUTHOR	COMPOSER
176	Roller Skating	Adapted	Hungarian Dance Tune
102	Rolling King	Traditional	Capstan Chantey
17	Rosina	Translated	French Singing Game
50	Row Your Boat	Traditional	American Round
75	Sad Mother Nature	J. W. Beattie	J. Wolverton
162	Sandman, The	Translated	Brahms
174	Saturday	Adapted	Hungarian Dance Tune
73	Scotland's Burning	Traditional	American Round
55	Sea Shell	Amy Lowell	J. Wolverton
14	Shake That Little Foot	Traditional	American Ballad
54	Ship, The	Adapted	Breton Folk Song
149	Siembamba	Translated	South African Folk Song
82	Silent Night	Joseph Mohr	Franz Gruber
9	Sing and Dance	Julie Gibault	Czech Folk Dance
147	Sing to God	Adapted	Joseph Pleyl
63	Sliding	Adapted	Philip Hayes
173	Slovak Dance	Adapted	Slovak Dance Tune
15	Slumber Song	Translated	Chilean Lullaby
119	Snow Feathers	Adapted	Bohemian Folk Song
110	Snowbird, The	Florence Meeker	Grace V. Wilson
49	Spinning Song	Translated	Norwegian Folk Song
174	Spring	Adapted	Netherlands Folk Song
157	Spring Awakes	Adapted	German Folk Song
193	Spring Birds	Adapted	German Folk Song
122	St. Valentine's Day	Shakespeare	English Folk Song
198	Star-Spangled Banner, The	Francis Scott Key	John Stafford Smith
156	Streamliner, The	Ruth Wilson Kelsey	Grace V. Wilson
178	Street Calls	J. W. Beattie	Old Tune
159	Sunrise	Adapted	Liszt
21	Sunset	K. Stoll	Austrian Folk Song
189	Susie, Little Susie	Paraphrased	German Folk Song
74	Swedish Lullaby	Adapted	Swedish Folk Song
190	Swinging	Florence Meeker	Grace V. Wilson
72	Telling Time	M. W. Clark	M. W. Clark
78	Thanksgiving Day	Edna Becker	Grace V. Wilson
158	Thief, The	Translated	German Folk Song
30	Tidy-o	Traditional	Missouri Version
137	To Market	Adapted	J. J. Wachsmann
191	To the Woods	Evanston children	Evanston children
18	Tower on Guard, The	Translated	Uruguayan Singing Game
60	Traveler, The	Edna Becker	Grace V. Wilson
91	Trees in Winter	Adapted	Chopin
140	Two Friends	Adapted	Spanish Melody
128	Washington and Lincoln	Charles Crane	Russel Godfrey
134	Weather Vane, The	Adapted	Beethoven
164	Welcome to Spring	Adapted	French Folk Song
182	What Can the Matter Be?	Traditional	English Folk Song
11	White Butterflies	Swinburne	Rossetter G. Cole
90	Winter Sports	Adapted	A. Maillart
93	Winter Visitor, The	Unknown	J. Wolverton
79	Winter Winds	Lloyd Norlin	Lloyd Norlin
126	Wise Ben Franklin	Lloyd Norlin	Lloyd Norlin
45	Wood-wind Duet, A	Adapted	Mozart
146	Yellow Hair	Translated	Ute (Indian) Song
86	Yule Nisse	Translated	Danish Folk Song